LADDERS *to* SUCCESS

on t...
Asse...

LEVEL **D**

Reading

LEVELED INSTRUCTION AND PRACTICE ON 10 ESSENTIAL SKILLS

ACKNOWLEDGMENTS

"Baby Hippo Adopted by Giant Tortoise" contains quotations courtesy of news.bbc.co.uk and Reuters

"Stolen Sports Car Found After 37 Years" contains quotations courtesy of www.nytimes.com and *The New York Post*

"Philadelphia Schools Say 'No' to Soda" contains quotations courtesy of Reuters

"$20 'Banana' Bill Sells for $25,300" contains quotations courtesy of The Associated Press

"Land of 1,000 Jokes" contains quotations courtesy of The Associated Press

"Malaysia Team to Track 'Bigfoot'" contains quotations courtesy of The Associated Press

"'Hogzilla'" contains quotations courtesy of The Associated Press

"Stick Ship" contains quotations courtesy of www.timeforkids.com

"Whale Lost on Delaware River" contains quotations courtesy of www.nefsc.noaa.gov/press_release/2005

Page 13-Hippo and Turtle, Peter Greste/Corbis

Page 20-Kishan Shrikanth, Amy Vitale/Getty Images

Page 55-Indoor Skiing and Snowboarding, Christof Koepsel/Getty Images

Page 62-Steve Fossett's Plane, Getty Images

Page 76-Del Monte $20 Bill, Tony Gutierrez/Associated Press

Page 88-Automatic Floor Cleaner, Doug McFadd/Getty Images

Page 97-Mayor of Normal, Seth Perlman/Associated Press

Page 104-Wet Cat, GK Hart and Vikki Hart/Getty Images

Page 105-Jackson Pollock, Martha Holmes/Getty Images

Page 111-Bigfoot, Antonio Barbagallo/VEER/Getty Images

Page 125-Swimming, John Todd/Corbis

Page 139-Willis Avenue Bridge, Rudy Sulgan/Corbis

Page 146-Beluga Whale, Brian Skerry/Getty Images

Ladders to Success, Reading Level D
178NA
ISBN-10: 1-59823-460-9
ISBN-13: 978-1-59823-460-2

Cover Image: Sam Ward/Mendola Artists

Triumph Learning® 136 Madison Avenue, 7th Floor, New York, NY 10016
Kevin McAliley, President and Chief Executive Officer

Table of Contents

Letter to the Student

Dear Student,

Welcome to **Ladders to Success** for Level D. This book will help you work on the ten reading skills most important to you this year. There is one lesson for each skill. You will master all ten skills by working through all ten lessons one by one.

This book does not rush you through a skill. Each lesson is fourteen pages long. This gives you plenty of time to really get comfortable learning what each skill means. You will see how each skill works in stories of different lengths.

The first page of every lesson is called Show What You Know. Take this short quiz to see how much you know about a skill before digging into the lesson. The next section, Guided Instruction 1, will start you off with some friendly guided review and practice. Practice the Skill 1, which follows Guided Instruction 1, shows you how to answer a multiple-choice question before asking you to try more by yourself. The next section, News Flash, is an exciting news story. It also comes with an activity.

Following the first News Flash is a three-page section called Ladder to Success. This section will give you three chances to practice the skill. Each practice is a little harder as you go "up the ladder." Now you are ready for the second part of the lesson.

The second part of the lesson is just like the first. You will see Guided Instruction 2, Practice the Skill 2, and another News Flash. This time around, these sections are a little harder. The last two pages of each lesson are called Show What You Learned. Show off everything you learned in the lesson by correctly answering multiple-choice questions on the skill. Words that are boldfaced in the lessons appear in the glossary at the back of the book.

The lessons in this book will help you practice and improve your skills. They will also get you ready for the tests you will be taking this year. Some of the practice will be in the style of the state test. You will be answering multiple-choice and open-ended questions. You may see questions like these on your state test. Practicing with these types of questions will build your confidence.

We hope you will enjoy using *Ladders to Success.* We want you to climb the ladder to success this year. This book will help you get started!

Letter to the Family

Dear Parent or Family Member,

The **Ladders to Success** series of workbooks is designed to prepare your child to master ten of the fundamental skills in reading that are essential for success, both in the curriculum and on state tests. *Ladders to Success* provides guided review and practice for the skills that are the building blocks of your child's education in reading. These are also the skills that will be tested on the state test in English Language Arts. Your child's success will be measured by how well he or she masters these skills.

Ladders to Success is a unique program in that each lesson is organized to ensure your child's success. Ten skills that students often find challenging are treated individually in ten lessons. Students are guided and supported through the first part of each lesson until they are ready to take on unguided practice in the second part of the lesson. Each lesson is fourteen pages long to give the student ample opportunity to review and practice a skill until a comfort level is reached. Support is gradually withdrawn throughout the lesson to build your student's confidence for independent work at the end of each lesson.

We invite you to be our partner in making learning a priority in your child's life. To help ensure success, we suggest that you review the lessons in this book with your child. You will see how each lesson gets subtly but progressively harder as you go along. While teachers will guide your child through the book in class, your support at home, added to the support of guided instruction and practice in the series, is vital to your child's comprehension.

We ask you to work with us this year to help your young student climb the ladder to success. Together, we can make a difference!

Letter to the Teacher

Dear Teacher,

Welcome to **Ladders to Success** in Reading for Level D. The Ladders to Success series of workbooks for reading is designed to prepare your students to master ten fundamental, grade-appropriate skills in reading that are essential for success both in the curriculum and on your state tests. Ladders provides guided review and practice for the skills that are the building blocks of the students' education. These are also skills that will be tested on your state tests in reading.

Ladders to Success is a unique program in that each lesson is leveled, or scaffolded, to ensure your students' success. Students are guided and supported through the first part of each lesson until they are ready to take on unguided practice in the second part of the lesson. Ten important skills are treated individually in ten lessons. Each lesson is fourteen pages long to give the student ample opportunity to review and practice a skill until a comfort level is reached. Support is slowly withdrawn throughout the lesson to build your students' confidence for independent work at the end of each lesson.

Ladders has a consistent, symmetrical format. The format is predictable from lesson to lesson, which increases students' comfort level with the presentation of skills-based information and practice. The first page of every lesson is called Show What You Know. This is a short diagnostic quiz to determine how much a student knows about a particular skill before digging into the lesson. It represents a snapshot of where each student is "now" before additional review and practice. This diagnostic quiz can be your guide in the way you choose to use the different parts of the lesson that follows.

The next section, Guided Instruction 1, will start students off slowly with guided review and practice. Practice the Skill 1, which immediately follows Guided Instruction 1, models how to answer a multiple-choice question before asking students to try more by themselves. The next section, News Flash, is an exciting contemporary news story that will engage students' interest. It is accompanied by an activity, often a graphic organizer, under the heading Write About It.

Following the first News Flash is a three-page section called Ladder to Success, which embodies the spirit of the Ladders series. This section provides three more chances to practice the skill. What makes this section unique is that each practice is a little harder as students go "up the ladder." By the time students have finished the third practice, they are ready for the second part of the lesson, which mirrors the first part. The Ladder to Success section is the crucial bridge between the first part of the lesson and the second.

Thus, you will now see Guided Instruction 2, Practice the Skill 2, and another News Flash. This time around, however, these sections are more challenging. The passages are longer and/or cognitively more difficult and there is less modeling. The activity under the Write About It heading in the second News Flash in each lesson, for example, is an unscaffolded writing activity.

The last two pages of each lesson represent a Posttest on the skill of the lesson. It is called Show What You Learned. Here is the student's chance to show off everything he or she learned in the lesson by successfully answering multiple-choice questions on the skill. The Posttest ends with an open-ended question, giving students the opportunity to show a deeper understanding of the skill now that they have completed the lesson. Words that are bold-faced in the lessons appear in the glossary at the back of the book.

Triumph Learning supports you in the difficult challenges you face in engaging your students in the learning process. *Ladders to Success* attempts to address some of these challenges by providing lessons that contain interesting material; scaffolded, or leveled, support; and a spectrum of multiple-choice questions and open-ended activities. This will allow students to build their confidence as they work toward proficiency with each skill in each lesson.

We ask you to work with us this year to help your students climb the ladder to success. Together, we *will* make a difference!

Show What You Know

Before you begin this lesson, take this quiz to show what you know about comparing and contrasting. Read this article about two pets. Then answer the questions.

Bumblebee and Dandelion

Last spring, the animal shelter had lots of kittens. My sister Ann begged Mom to let her have one. Finally, Mom agreed. Ann picked out one with black and white stripes. She named it Bumblebee. I like that name. Those stripes made the kitten look like a bumblebee. Now Bumblebee sleeps on Ann's bed. She likes to play with a little green ball. Most of all, she likes to chase birds and field mice. I hope she never catches one, though.

Seeing Bumblebee made me want a pet, too. I didn't want a cat, though. I wanted a dog. Mom agreed. At the animal shelter, I found a yellow, fuzzy puppy. I knew at once that I wanted her! Her fuzzy hair made me think of a dandelion, so that's what I named her. I really love Dandelion. She sleeps on my bed at night. She likes to play with a stuffed monkey toy. Most of all, she likes to chase Bumblebee!

Circle the letter of the best answer.

1. Bumblebee and Dandelion are alike because they —

    A are both cats

    B are both dogs

    C like to play with stuffed monkey toys

    D both came from the animal shelter

2. Both Bumblebee and Dandelion —

    A chase things

    B have stripes

    C sleep on Ann's bed at night

    D are fuzzy and yellow

3. How are Bumblebee and Dandelion different from each other?

    A Bumblebee is a girl animal, and Dandelion is a boy animal.

    B Bumblebee likes to chase field mice and Dandelion does not.

    C Only Dandelion likes to sleep on a person's bed.

    D Only Dandelion was named after something she looks like.

4. Which statement is true only about Dandelion?

    A Dandelion came from a shelter.

    B Dandelion is named after something she looks like.

    C Dandelion is fuzzy and yellow.

    D Dandelion likes to play with a toy.

Introduction

When you **compare** things, you tell how they are the same. When you **contrast** things, you tell how they are different.

To compare and contrast when you read,

- Look for clue words that tell how things are alike and different. Clue words such as *like, both,* and *too* show how things are similar. The clue words *different, unlike, but,* and *on the other hand* show differences.

- Use the clue words to find how the subjects are compared and contrasted.

Here's How

Read these sentences. Use clue words to compare and contrast the Rocky Mountains and the Appalachian Mountains.

The Rocky Mountains are some of the tallest and most beautiful mountains in the United States. These mountains, in the western part of the country, rise up to 14,000 feet high and beyond. The Appalachian Mountains, on the other hand, are less than half as tall.

Think About It

1. The phrase *on the other hand* is a sign of a contrast between mountain ranges.

2. Using the clue words, I see that one difference between the mountain ranges is that the Appalachian Mountains are less than half as tall as the Rocky Mountains.

Use Prior Knowledge

When you **use prior knowledge,** you think about what you already know about what you are reading.

- Read the title and look at any pictures. Think of what you know about the topic. Use what you know to help you understand the ideas.

- Think about things that are compared or contrasted. Use what you know to help you understand how they are similar or different.

Read this passage. Use the Reading Guide for tips that can help you to use prior knowledge to compare and contrast as you read.

Reading Guide

Read the title and the first paragraph. Think about what you already know about mountain ranges.

Think about the mountain ranges that are described. Find what qualities are compared and contrasted.

Look for clue words that point to similarities and differences.

MOUNTAINS BIG AND SMALL

The Rocky Mountains are some of the tallest and most beautiful mountains in the United States. These mountains, in the western part of the country, rise up to 14,000 feet high and beyond. The Appalachian Mountains, on the other hand, are less than half as tall. Did you know that long ago the Appalachians may have been as tall as the Rockies are today?

The Appalachians, in the eastern United States, are some of the oldest mountains in the world. They were formed when two great land masses **collided** about 680 million years ago. Over millions of years, weather caused the mountains to wear down. Today, the tallest mountain in the range is 6,684 feet tall.

The Rocky Mountains, on the other hand, are newer, with some having formed less than 100 million years ago. They were also formed by land masses crashing into each other. Like the Appalachians, the Rocky Mountains will also be slowly eroded. Millions of years from now, they will completely disappear. Until then, enjoy the view!

Now use what you learned to compare and contrast.

Answer the questions on the next page.

Practice the Skill 1

Practice comparing and contrasting the two mountain ranges in the passage you just read.

EXAMPLE

In the past, the Appalachian Mountains may have been —

A in the same place as the Rocky Mountains are today

B much taller than the Rocky Mountains are today

C as tall as the Rocky Mountains are today

D as tall as the Rocky Mountains were millions of years ago

Find places where the two subjects are described.

The Appalachians from long ago and the Rocky Mountains of today are compared in the first paragraph.

Review the passage to find clues that tell how things are alike and different.

The phrase *as tall as* is a clue that signals a comparison.

Use the clues to help you find how the two subjects are compared and contrasted.

The passage states that in the past, the Appalachian Mountains may have been as tall as the Rocky Mountains are today.

Now read each question. Circle the letter of the best answer.

1. One way the Appalachian Mountains are different from the Rocky Mountains is —

   A the Appalachians are in the eastern part of the country

   B the Appalachians are in the western part of the country

   C the Appalachians are millions of years old

   D the Appalachians are beautiful

2. The Rocky Mountains are —

   A older than the Appalachians

   B narrower than the Appalachians

   C smaller than the Appalachians

   D newer than the Appalachians

3. What is one way the Rocky Mountains and Appalachian Mountains are the same?

   A their age

   B their height

   C the way they were formed

   D the way they look now

4. Both the Rocky Mountains and the Appalachian Mountains —

   A will not be affected by erosion

   B will one day disappear

   C will continue to grow taller

   D will one day collide

Baby Hippo Adopted by Giant Tortoise

Owen the baby hippo and Mzee the giant tortoise are snuggling with each other.

MOMBASA, KENYA—A baby hippo and a giant tortoise have formed an unlikely friendship. Owen, a 1-year-old hippo, and Mzee, a 120-year-old tortoise, live together in an animal sanctuary. They have been found eating, sleeping, and walking around with each other. According to one park official, the pair "have become **inseparable**."

The story of Owen and Mzee did not start out happily. Kenyan residents found Owen wandering the African plains after a severe flood. He was **orphaned** during the storm and was very weak. Wildlife rangers soon rescued the 600-pound hippo and brought him to a wildlife **sanctuary**. There, Owen met Mzee, and the two soon became friends.

Park officials believe that Owen may have been looking for a mother in the old, cranky male tortoise. Mzee has "a dark gray color, similar to grown up hippos," explained sanctuary employee Sabine Baer.

Owen may find a new mother soon. The sanctuary plans to place Owen with a lonely female hippo named Cleo when he gets older. Until then, Owen and Mzee will remain the best of friends.

Write About It

How are Owen and Mzee different from each other? In what ways are they similar? Use this graphic organizer to compare and contrast the two animals.

Owen	Mzee
Both	

Review

You have learned that to **compare** things, you tell how they are alike. To **contrast** things, you tell how they are different. You can use clues from the text to help you compare and contrast.

Review the steps you can use to compare and contrast.

- Read the passage to find related things that are compared and contrasted.
- Look for clue words. Words such as *like, both, also,* and *same* are used to compare. Words such as *different, unlike, but,* and *however* are used to contrast.
- Use the clue words to find ways things are similar and different.

Practice 1

Read the following passage. As you read, think about what you already know about how July and September are alike and different. Look for clue words that help you to compare and contrast.

> My favorite month is July. I like it because the weather is warm, and you have vacation all month. I can go swimming at the pool. September is my second favorite. It's a warm month too, but it's too cool for the pool. Another neat thing is that the leaves start changing colors. The only thing I don't like is that it's the month when vacation ends!

Use this Venn diagram. In the first circle, write ideas about July. In the second circle, write ideas about September. In the middle, write ideas that fit both July and September.

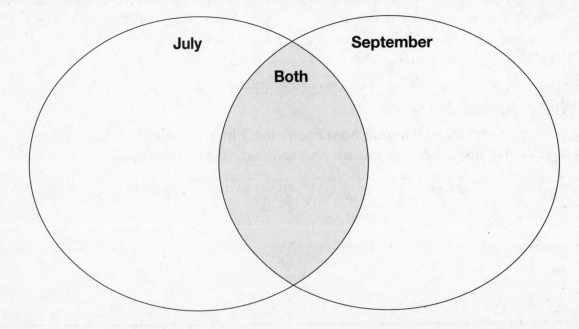

Practice 2

Read the story. How are Ted and Ramon alike and different?

Ted didn't like being new in town. He missed his old friends, and he felt lonely. Then he saw a sign for a stamp club on the school bulletin board. Ted had collected stamps for two years. He decided to join the club. He hoped to meet some new friends there.

Unlike Ted, Ramon had lived in town for years. He felt lonely, though. None of his friends collected stamps. Like Ted, Ramon had collected stamps for about two years. That's why he decided to start a stamp club. When he hung the sign on the school bulletin board, he felt happy. Maybe new people would join the club. Maybe he would meet a new friend.

Use this graphic organizer to compare and contrast Ted and Ramon.

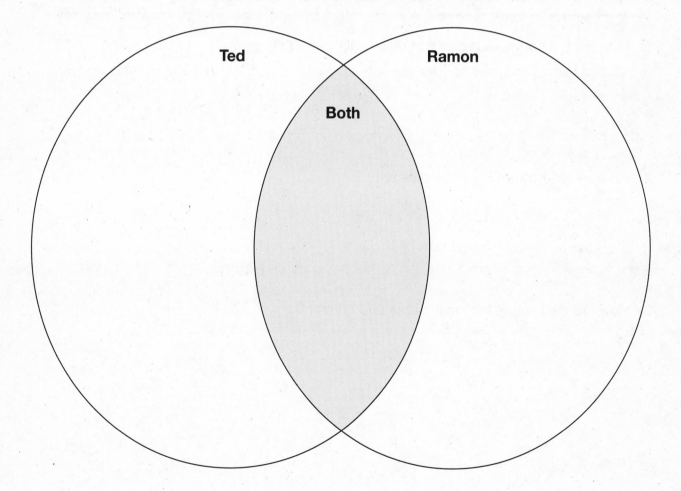

Practice 3

Read the passage. Then compare and contrast crows and ravens in a graphic organizer and answer the questions. Create the graphic organizer on a separate sheet of paper.

Crows are shiny black birds. They are about 17 inches long. Thousands of crows may travel together. They build their nests high up in trees. They eat grains, insects, and dead animals. Crows have a simple call: "caw, caw." Some have learned to speak human words. Some have even learned to count. They can live to be 20 years old.

Ravens are also shiny black birds. Like crows, their feathers shine with blue or purple streaks. Ravens are about 26 inches long. They travel in pairs and build their nests high up in trees. They eat grains, insects, mice, and dead animals. Ravens make many croaks, gurgles, and deep "caws." Scientists think that each sound is like a word. It has a special meaning. Ravens have learned to speak human words, too. They have been known to live 69 years.

1. How are the bodies of crows and ravens alike and different?

_____

_____

2. How are their habits alike and different?

_____

_____

3. How are the sounds they make alike and different?

_____

_____

LADDERS
to SUCCESS

LESSON

1

Comparing and
Contrasting

Guided Instruction 2

Introduction

Writers often **compare and contrast** subjects. They tell us how things are alike and different. Clue words help readers understand how things are alike and different.

As you saw on pages 13–15, a graphic organizer can help you compare and contrast.

- In the left circle, write ideas that are only true for the first subject.
- In the right circle, write ideas that are only true for the second subject.
- In the middle section where the two circles meet, write ideas that are true for both subjects.

Here's How

Read these sentences. What fact is true about Andy, but not the narrator?

Andy sings well, too. However, when I sing, people cover their ears. Even our dog Harry leaves the room!

Think About it

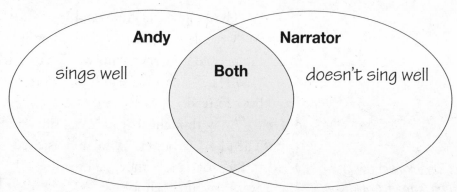

Try This Strategy

Monitor and Clarify

When you **monitor and clarify,** you check to make sure that you understand what you are reading.

- At the end of each paragraph, stop reading. Think about what you just read.
- State the important ideas in your own words. If you can't, reread the paragraph.
- Watch for ways the article changes. Does the author move on to new ideas or events?

Read the story. Use the Reading Guide for tips that can help you monitor and clarify and compare and contrast as you read.

Reading Guide

Think about what you read in the first paragraph. How is Andy different from the narrator?

What clue words in this paragraph help you to find other differences?

Think back about what you have read. Could you explain why Harry is a different kind of helper than the narrator is?

A Different Kind of Helper

My brother Andy is in the second grade. He doesn't read well. I'm in fourth grade, and I'm a really good reader. So I tried to help Andy, but he got mad when I corrected him. "You make me feel dumb!" he'd wail.

I didn't mean to make him feel dumb. He's smart. He's good at lots of things, too. He's a better soccer player than I am. Andy sings well, too. However, when I sing, people cover their ears. Even our dog Harry leaves the room!

Both Andy and I really like Harry. We've had him since Andy was born. Back then, Harry liked to protect Andy. Harry still follows Andy wherever he goes. They often sit quietly together. Harry never leaves the room when Andy sings!

Thinking about Andy and Harry gave me an idea. Andy needed to practice his reading in a comfortable way. He needed a listener who wouldn't correct him. So I said, "Do Harry a favor. Read him a story. He doesn't know how to read."

Andy thought that idea was silly. He thought about it. Then he tried it. Harry sat and listened to the story. Now they read stories every day after school. Andy's reading has improved. And Harry has heard some really good stories.

> **Answer the questions on the next page.**

Practice the Skill 2

Practice comparing and contrasting by answering questions about the story you just read. Read each question. Circle the letter of the best answer.

1. Which statement is true about both Andy and the narrator?

   A They are not good soccer players.
   B They are good singers.
   C They like to read stories to their dog.
   D They really like their dog.

2. Which statement is true about the narrator, but not true about Andy?

   A He is in fourth grade.
   B He has a dog named Harry.
   C He has an older brother.
   D He sings well.

3. Which statement is true about Andy, but not true about the narrator?

   A He needs to practice his singing.
   B He needs to work on his reading.
   C He needs to work harder at soccer.
   D He needs to stop correcting his brother.

4. Which word from the passage shows how two things are similar?

   A however
   B both
   C better
   D good

5. How is Harry different from the narrator?

   A He likes Andy.
   B He doesn't like Andy's singing, and leaves the room when he sings.
   C He makes Andy feel dumb.
   D He sits quietly while Andy reads, and he doesn't correct him.

6. Harry has been Andy's pal since Andy was a baby. On a separate sheet of paper, tell about the similarities and differences between the ways Harry and the narrator each might treat Andy.

BANGALORE, INDIA—Cut! Kishan Shrikanth, who is 10 years old, recently finished directing his first film. The India-born moviemaker is set to become the world's youngest **director**. His nickname has become Master Kishan.

Kishan has already starred in 24 films, but this is his first time directing. He learned how to make movies by talking to directors of the films in which he acted. He also read many books about moviemaking to prepare him for the task.

The film "Care of Footpath" is about the street children of India. Their only address is the city **footpaths** where they sleep. "I felt very bad and thought I must do something for them," Kishan told the BBC. Kishan wrote the film himself, and also stars in it with several of India's top actors.

Kishan's movie career keeps him busy. However, he still finds time for school. The young director has his friends take notes when he is away. He is confident that he will pass his tests and be promoted from the fifth grade.

Kishan Shrikanth has been either directing or acting in movies since he was 4 years old.

The World's Youngest Movie Director

Write About It

Now you will practice the skill using a real news story. Write a paragraph about how Kishan is similar to and different from other kids his age. Use facts from the article.

Read this article about tall trees. Then answer the questions on the next page.

EXTREME TREES

California is home to some of the most amazing living things of the world. Along the northern coast of the state, the sequoias and the redwoods stand tall. These trees are bigger and taller than any other living thing. These two kinds of trees are closely related, and they have a similar history. Both were once found around the world. Today, they are mostly seen in California.

The redwood is the tallest tree in the world. It can grow to more than 350 feet high. That's taller than the Statue of Liberty! While redwoods can live in many areas, they only reach this height in a foggy area of California, where other trees do not crowd them out.

While redwoods may be taller, giant sequoias are the largest trees ever to live. This is because of their width. They can grow up to 30 feet wide. One sequoia was wide enough that cars could drive through it! Like redwoods, they are very tall. They can grow 300 feet high.

Sequoias grow faster than any other tree. They can grow one or two feet per year until they reach their top height. Then they continue to grow wider. Each year, they create as much wood as one 50-foot-tall tree that is one foot wide.

Sequoias also live a very long time, up to 3,000 years. Only one other kind of tree lives longer—the bristlecone pine. This tree is found in another part of California. It is not nearly as big or as tall as sequoias or redwoods. It only reaches 60 feet high. However, some bristlecone pines have lived longer than anything else on earth. They can live 4,000 years. This means that they were seedlings when the ancient pyramids of Egypt were being built. They may not be big, but they sure know how to survive!

Read each question. Circle the letter of the best answer.

1. Both the sequoia and the redwood —

   A can grow 300 feet high
   B can live 3,000 years
   C are found around the world
   D are the same kind of tree

2. What is one difference between sequoias and redwoods?

   A Redwoods are taller.
   B Redwoods live longer.
   C Redwoods live in California.
   D Redwoods are found in forests.

3. In this passage, the Statue of Liberty is used to —

   A compare its height to a bristlecone pine's
   B compare its weight to a sequoia's
   C compare its height to a sequoia's
   D compare its height to a redwood's

4. One difference between bristlecone pines and the other trees described in the passage is —

   A bristlecone pines do not live as long
   B bristlecone pines were once found around the world
   C bristlecone pines live longer than many other trees
   D bristlecone pines are found along California's northern coast

5. Both the bristlecone pine and the sequoia —

   A are taller than the redwood
   B are bigger than the redwood
   C live longer than the redwood
   D have more leaves than the redwood

6. What is one difference between sequoias and the other trees described in the passage?

   A Sequoias are thinner than the other trees.
   B Sequoias grow faster than the other trees.
   C Sequoias are taller than the other trees.
   D Sequoias live longer than the other trees.

7. One fact about these trees that is not compared or contrasted is —

   A their size
   B their height
   C their color
   D their age

8. Choose two of the kinds of trees described in this article. Compare and contrast them, using facts from the article.

Before you begin this lesson, take this quiz to show what you know about sequence. Read this passage about a girl's schedule. Then answer the questions.

MY BUSY SATURDAY

Saturdays are really busy since school started in August. My day starts very early in the morning with my soccer game. I play goalie, and it's really fun. Next, my mom takes my brother Jacob and me out for a late breakfast. After that, we drop Jacob off at his flute lesson. Then Mom and I go grocery shopping. On the way back home for lunch, we pick up Jacob. And that's just the morning!

After lunch we have some free time to play outside. Sometimes my friend Miles comes over. When we come back inside Mom makes us do our homework so we don't have to worry about it on Sunday. I usually grumble about it, until she gives me "the look." Then I get to work.

At the end of the day we all pitch in and make dinner. After dinner, we pick a movie and curl up on the couch to watch it. Finally, it's time for bed. I think Saturdays are great!

Circle the letter of the best answer.

1. What happens first on Saturdays?

   A late breakfast

   B soccer game

   C flute lesson

   D grocery shopping

2. When do they go grocery shopping?

   A before the soccer game

   B before breakfast

   C after dropping Jacob off

   D after free time

3. What do the kids do before homework time?

   A play outside

   B watch a movie

   C make dinner

   D go to bed

4. The last activity of the day is —

   A grocery shopping

   B watching a movie

   C playing with Miles

   D Jacob's flute lesson

LADDERS
to SUCCESS

LESSON
2
Understanding
Sequence

Guided Instruction 1

Sequence is the order in which things happen. When you use **sequence,** you put events in the order in which they happened. You can better understand what you read if you know what happened first, next, and last.

To understand sequence,

- Read to find out what happens in the passage.
- Then think about the order of the events. What happened first? Next? Last?
- Look for clue words to help put events in order. Some are *first, next, last, then, before,* and *after.* Look for words that show when something happened in time, such as *next week, in a month,* and *a year later.*

Here's How

Read these sentences. Use clue words to understand the sequence of events.

Aunt Sue and I had fun all day. First, we rode horses. Next, we picked corn. After lunch, we read books. Then we went for a swim.

Think About It

1. *The person in the story is describing what happened during the day.*

2. *I see that they rode horses, picked corn, read books, and went for a swim.*

3. *I know the order because I notice the words first, next, after, and then. Those words help me put the events of the day in order.*

Summarize

When you **summarize,** you think about the main ideas and events in a passage.

- As you read each paragraph, state the important ideas in you own words.
- Think of the order in which events happened. Look back if you have trouble.

Read this passage. Use the Reading Guide for tips that can help you to summarize and understand sequence.

Reading Guide

Read to find out what events happen in the story.

Look for clue words that will help you put the events in order.

Summarize the main events. Make sure they are in the right order.

A Weekend at Aunt Sue's Farm

Last month, I spent a weekend with Aunt Sue. She lives on a big farm.

Mom and I got to Aunt Sue's on Friday night, after driving all day. We were tired, but not too tired to eat. Aunt Sue served my favorite dinner—macaroni and cheese. After I ate, I went right to bed.

On Saturday morning, Mom got ready to drive to Ohio. She wanted to visit my grandparents. Before she left, we went to the barn to collect eggs. Then we cooked breakfast for Aunt Sue. After that, Mom said goodbye.

Aunt Sue and I had fun all day. First, we rode horses. Next, we picked corn. After lunch, we read books. Finally, we went for a swim.

On Sunday, I helped Aunt Sue weed her flower garden. Just before lunch, Mom returned. After lunch, she and I started our long ride home. It was a great weekend!

Now use what you learned to understand sequence.

Answer the questions on the next page.

Practice the Skill 1

Practice understanding the sequence of events in the passage you just read.

EXAMPLE

On Friday night, what did the boy do after he ate dinner?

A He collected eggs.

B He and his mother drove a long way.

C He arrived at Aunt Sue's house.

D He went to bed.

Read to find out what happens in the passage.

The second paragraph tells me what the boy did on Friday night.

Then think about the order of the events. What happened first? Next? Last?

First, the boy and his mother drove a long way. Then they arrived at Aunt Sue's. Next, they ate dinner.

Look for clue words to help you put events in order.

I read the phrase after I ate and see that the boy went to bed after dinner.

Now read each question. Circle the letter of the best answer.

1. What was the first thing the boy did on Saturday morning?

    A He said goodbye to his mother.

    B He cooked breakfast for Aunt Sue.

    C He collected eggs.

    D He rode horses.

2. What was the last thing that he and Aunt Sue did Saturday afternoon?

    A They rode horses.

    B They went for a swim.

    C They picked corn.

    D They read books.

3. What did the boy do on Sunday, before his mother returned?

    A He ate lunch.

    B He read books.

    C He planted a garden.

    D He weeded the garden.

4. Which clue word tells when his mother returned?

    A *before* lunch

    B *after* lunch

    C *next* day

    D *earlier* that day

Alan Poster's Corvette was originally painted blue. When it was found, it was painted silver.

Stolen Sports Car Found After 37 Years

LOS ANGELES, CA—Thirty-seven years after it was reported missing, a stolen Corvette was finally found. The sports car was returned to its original owner, Alan Poster. "We can call this a miracle," Poster said.

Poster bought the car in 1969. He was living in New York. It was stolen from his garage shortly after he bought it. Later, Poster moved to California. He thought the car was gone forever. Then, almost 40 years later, the car was found. It was in a **container ship** headed to Sweden. The Corvette was returned to Mr. Poster a few months after its discovery.

The original thief would have a hard time stealing the car a second time. Poster, now 63, is not letting the car out of his sight. "It's not getting away from me again," Poster said.

Write About It

In this article, the events are not written in time order. In what order did they actually take place? List the events. Then number them to show the sequence.

	Events

Ladder to Success

Review

You have learned that sequencing means to put events in order. As you read, think about the order in which things happen.

Review the steps you can use to understand sequence.

- Think about the events that happen in the passage.
- Think about what happened first, next, and last.
- Look for clue words such as *then, before,* and *after.* You can also look for time words and phrases such as *next week, in a month,* and *a year later.*

Practice 1

Read the following passage. As you read, look for clue words that help you to understand the sequence, or order, of events. Look for other clue words that tell about the passing of time.

> The dentist says you should brush your teeth after every meal. Follow these simple steps for healthy teeth! First, **moisten** the bristles of the toothbrush. Then squeeze on a dab of toothpaste. Next, brush your teeth. First brush up and down and then brush side to side. After you finish your teeth, brush your tongue. Then, rinse your mouth with water. Finally, dry your face with a towel.

Now think about the order of the events. Fill in this graphic organizer by writing the events in sequence.

1	
2	
3	
4	
5	
6	
7	

Practice 2

Read these directions for making biscuits. Notice the clue words. What do they tell you about the order in which things happen?

It's easy and fun to make **biscuits.** First, turn on the oven so it heats up. Next, take out the flour, baking soda, **shortening,** salt, and milk. Then mix the **ingredients** to make the batter. Once the batter is mixed well, form it into balls and set them on a baking pan. After that, slide the pan into the oven. Don't forget to set the timer to thirty minutes! While the biscuits are cooking, clean up any mess you made. After thirty minutes, the timer will go off and you can carefully take the hot pan out of the oven. It's best to eat the biscuits while they're warm. Try them with butter and jam!

Use this graphic organizer to show the steps for making biscuits. Be sure to write the sequence of events in the correct order.

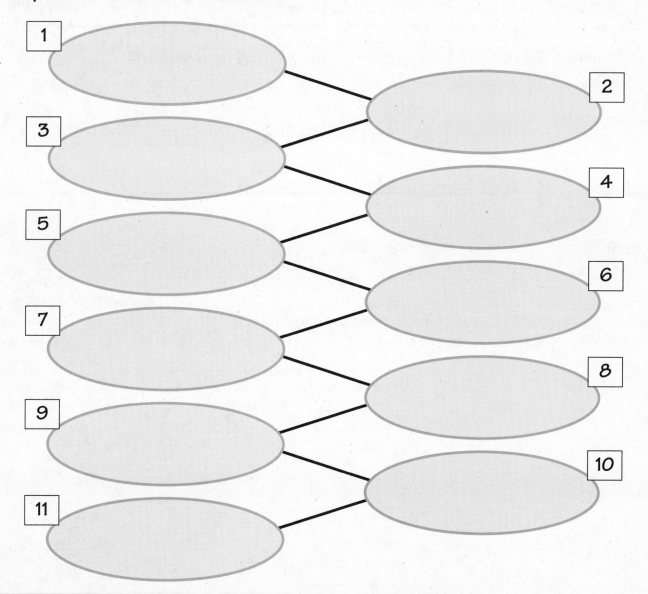

Practice 3

Read the passage. Then use the clue words to understand the order in which things happen. Make a graphic organizer on a separate sheet of paper to organize your thoughts.

In June, my baby sister Maria was born. A month later, Mom and Dad said, "Manny, we're thinking of moving to a bigger house."

So I said, "What for? This apartment is big enough, and all my friends live on our block. Why would we want to move?"

Dad looked at me and smiled. Then he said, "Hey! Who's asking these questions? Aren't you the boy who told me last week that he wanted a big backyard?"

Then it was my turn to smile. "Can we really have a big yard? When are we moving?"

"I'd really like a yard, too," Mom answered. Then she gave me a hug. After I started to feel really excited about the move, she said, "But we're going to have to buy a rake, and you're going to have to learn how to rake leaves, pal!"

1. Did Mom and Dad want to move before or after the baby was born?

_____

_____

2. When did Manny say that he wanted to have a big yard?

_____

_____

3. What did Mom say after Manny got excited about moving?

_____

_____

Guided Instruction 2

Introduction

Sequence is the order in which things happen. Writers often use clue words to make the order of events clear. Some of those clue words are *first, next, then, before, after,* and *last.* Writers will also use words and phrases that tell about the passing of time, such as *before breakfast, two years ago,* and *yesterday.*

As you saw on pages 27–29, a sequence chart can help you put events in order.

- Use clue words to find the first event in the sequence. Write it in the first space on the chart. Then find the next event. Write it in the second space.

- Continue using clue words to figure out the right order. Continue writing each event in the correct space on the chart.

Here's How

Read these sentences. What is the correct sequence of events?

> After that, Granddad and his dad went to lots of games. One was in 1956. The Braves' star player was Hank Aaron. At that game, he hit a home run. Granddad caught the ball. After the game, Hank Aaron signed it!

Think About It

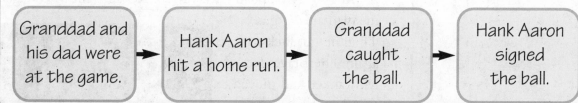

Granddad and his dad were at the game. → Hank Aaron hit a home run. → Granddad caught the ball. → Hank Aaron signed the ball.

Try This Strategy

Scan and Skim

When you **scan and skim,** you look over a piece of writing before you start to read it.

- Look over the passage and look at any pictures. What do you think the passage is about?

- Skim the passage for key words, including sequence clues. Think about what might happen in the passage.

Read the story. Use the Reading Guide for tips that can help you scan and skim each step in the sequence of events.

Reading Guide

Look over the words and picture. What do you think the story is about?

What words tell about dates and the passage of time?

What clue words in the third paragraph help you to understand the sequence of events?

THOSE GOOD OLD BRAVES!

Granddad has been a big baseball fan since he was a child. He likes one team best. They are the Braves.

Granddad was born in Milwaukee, Wisconsin. He became a Braves fan in 1952. He was only six years old back then. At that time, the team played in Boston. When Granddad turned seven, he got lucky. The Braves moved to Milwaukee!

After that, Granddad and his dad went to lots of games. One was in 1956. The Braves' star player was Hank Aaron. At that game, he hit a home run. Granddad caught the ball. After the game, Hank Aaron signed it!

In 1957, the Braves won the World Series. They beat the Yankees. For weeks after that, Granddad was really happy. The next year, the Braves returned to the World Series. Once more, they played the Yankees. This time, the Yankees won.

In 1965, Granddad left Milwaukee. He went to college in Atlanta, Georgia. Then he got lucky again. The Braves left Milwaukee and moved to Atlanta!

Granddad still lives in Atlanta. Whenever I visit him, we go to a Braves game together.

Answer the questions on the next page.

Practice understanding sequence by answering questions about the story you just read. Read each question. Circle the letter of the best answer.

1. What happened after Granddad turned seven?

   A   The Braves won the World Series.
   B   The Braves moved to Boston.
   C   The Braves moved to Milwaukee.
   D   The Braves moved to Atlanta.

2. What happened before Hank Aaron signed the baseball?

   A   Granddad hit a home run.
   B   Granddad went to the World Series.
   C   Granddad went to Atlanta.
   D   Granddad caught the ball.

3. What happened the year after the Braves won the World Series in 1957?

   A   The Braves lost the World Series.
   B   The Braves moved to Boston.
   C   The Yankees lost again.
   D   The Yankees moved to Atlanta.

4. Where did Granddad go after he left Milwaukee in 1965?

   A   to the World Series
   B   to college in Atlanta
   C   to visit Boston
   D   to see a game with his dad

5. What is the last move the Braves made?

   A   The Braves moved to Boston.
   B   The Braves moved to New York.
   C   The Braves moved to Atlanta.
   D   The Braves moved to Milwaukee.

6. On a separate sheet of paper, retell this story in your own words. You can use dates to help you put the events in sequence.

MOUNT RUSHMORE PRESIDENTS Get a Facial

Park rangers blasted Mount Rushmore with water to remove dirt and grime.

KEYSTONE, SD—Four of America's most famous faces received a much-needed **facial** recently. The presidents of Mount Rushmore were cleaned for the first time since they were carved in stone 65 years ago.

This was not your ordinary cleaning. First, park rangers attached cables above the stone faces of Presidents George Washington, Thomas Jefferson, Abraham Lincoln, and Theodore Roosevelt. Then, the rangers climbed down the stone faces to get as close as they could. Finally, they sprayed each face with a powerful blast of hot water.

The cleaning helped remove dirt and grime that had built up over the years. Over time, the dirt could have caused parts of Mount Rushmore to crumble.

The carving of Mount Rushmore began in 1927. It was designed by a famous sculptor named Gutzon Borglum. Borglum and his team used drills, hammers, **chisels,** and dynamite to carve the famous monument. The project took 14 years to finish.

Today more than 2 million people visit Mount Rushmore each year.

Write About It

Now you will practice the skill using a real news story. On a separate sheet of paper, write a paragraph explaining the three steps that were taken to clean Mount Rushmore.

Read this article about funny inventions. Then answer the questions on the next page.

WACKY INVENTIONS

Inventors have given us some great new things. For example, Thomas Edison gave us the electric light. What a bright idea that was!

Many inventors begin with a big idea. Then they draw sketches before building models. Next, they test each model. If a model doesn't work, they go back to their sketch pads. Then they build more models. When a model finally works, the inventor gets a **patent.** This is a legal paper that protects the inventor. It says, "This invention, on this date, is my big idea and no one else's!" The patent **ensures** that no one else claims credit for such a big, bright idea.

Some ideas are really useful, while others are just plain wacky. One inventor noticed that some people eat too much, so he got an idea. He thought that if people ate more slowly, they might eat less. So he invented an "alarm fork." Its patent is dated 1995. On the handle of the fork are a red light and a green light. To use the fork, you fill it with food. Next, you wait for the green light to shine. When it does, you put the food in your mouth. After that, the light turns red. You can load the fork with more food at any time. But you can't put the fork in your mouth until the green light comes on again. It can be a really long wait!

Do you like picnics? Another inventor had an idea that you might find interesting. He came up with a special picnic table with a built-in motor. Its patent is dated 2003. To use the table, you put the food and plates on it. Then ask everyone to sit down. Next, turn on the motor. Finally, drive the table to your favorite picnic spot!

Read each question. Circle the letter of the best answer.

1. What is the first step an inventor takes after thinking of an idea?

   A tests a model

   B gets a patent

   C draws a sketch

   D makes a model

2. What step does an inventor take if the model does not work?

   A retests the model

   B makes new sketches

   C gets a patent

   D gets a legal paper

3. What is the last important thing an inventor must do?

   A get a patent

   B make a model

   C sell the invention

   D think of a new idea

4. What must happen before someone can eat food with the alarm fork?

   A The green light must come on.

   B The red light must come on.

   C The alarm bell must ring.

   D The food must cool down.

5. What happens after you put the alarm fork in your mouth?

   A The light turns green.

   B The light turns red.

   C The alarm bell rings.

   D The table begins to move.

6. When can you put the fork back in your mouth?

   A before the red light comes on again

   B when you load your fork with food again

   C after the green light comes on again

   D when you are hungry again

7. What should you do after people sit down at the special picnic table?

   A turn on the motor

   B put the food on it

   C put the plates on it

   D show the patent

8. On a separate sheet of paper, explain the steps an inventor takes with an invention.

Show What You Know

Before you begin this lesson, take this quiz to show what you know about cause and effect. Read this passage about a dunk tank. Then answer the questions.

MR. JONES IN THE DUNK TANK

Our town has a carnival every year to raise money for charity. One of the most popular games at the carnival is the dunk tank. Someone sits over a tank of water. Someone else pays to throw a ball. If they hit the target with the ball, the other person falls into the tank of water. This year, everyone asked my teacher Mr. Jones to sit in the dunk tank. So, he agreed to do it.

He was late getting to the carnival because he had a flat tire on his way there. Most of us thought he wouldn't come at all. When he finally did arrive, I barely **recognized** him. It was the first time I had seen him wearing something besides a suit and tie.

He was soon sitting in the dunk tank. I made sure that I was the first person in line. I walked up to the dunk tank, grabbed a ball, and threw it. My aim was perfect. Mr. Jones fell right into the water with a splash because the ball hit the middle of the target. We both laughed. Next year, I want to be in the dunk tank.

Circle the letter of the best answer.

1. Why did Mr. Jones agree to be in the dunk tank?

    A He likes water.

    B He is a teacher.

    C Everyone asked him to do it.

    D Everyone told him it was fun.

2. Mr. Jones was late for the carnival because —

    A he was scared

    B he had a flat tire

    C he got lost on the way

    D he had to change clothes

3. Because Mr. Jones didn't wear a suit and tie, the narrator —

    A barely recognized him

    B told him he was late

    C asked him to get in the tank

    D asked him to hit the target

4. Why did Mr. Jones fall into the water?

    A The ball hit the middle of the target.

    B The narrator threw the ball very hard.

    C He slipped and fell into the water.

    D He was pushed into the water.

A **cause** is an event that makes something happen. The **effect** is what happens.

To recognize cause and effect,

- Look for details that tell what happens in the passage.

- Think about each event in the passage. Look for a cause for each event. Ask yourself, "Why did this happen?" Then find the effect.

- Look for clue words that tell you that something is a cause, such as *because, since,* and *if.* Look for clue words that tell you that something is an effect, such as *so, therefore,* and *as a result.*

Read this sentence. Use clue words and what you already know to recognize cause and effect.

Since Amir grows more carrots than he can eat, he sells some of them to our neighbors.

Think About It

1. I read to see what happened. I see that Amir sells carrots to his neighbors.

2. I think about why Amir sells the carrots.

3. The word *since* tells me that Amir growing more carrots than he can eat is the cause. Amir selling carrots to his neighbors is the effect.

Try This Strategy

Visualize

When you **visualize,** you picture a story in your mind.

- Carefully read how the author describes a person, place, thing, or event.

- Think about the words the author uses to describe these things.

- Imagine the story taking place as if it were a movie in your mind.

Read the story. Use the Reading Guide for tips that can help you visualize and recognize cause and effect as you read.

Reading Guide

Imagine what a garden with purple carrots looks like.

Think about why the narrator waters the garden.

Look for clue words that show cause or effect. The phrase As a result *signals an effect. Look for the effect it refers to. Also, look for the cause.*

Amir's PURPLE Carrots

My neighbor Amir has a garden in his backyard. His friends grow tomatoes and cucumbers in their gardens. Amir, however, grows something unusual. He grows purple carrots. Purple carrots are a special type of carrot that was grown in the Middle East before orange carrots were grown. He likes the bright color and sweet flavor of this special type of carrot. Since Amir grows more carrots than he can eat, he sells some of them to our neighbors.

Amir told me taking care of his garden is too much work for him to do alone, so I help him by watering his garden every day. If the plants aren't watered every day, they will die. I also pull weeds and pick the carrots.

Amir gives me some of the carrots that he grows for free because I help him so much. One time, I took the carrots to school. My friend said that purple carrots were really weird. As a result, nobody would even eat one. I ended up eating them all myself. Since I ate so many, I felt sick. I haven't eaten a purple carrot since. I still help Amir, but now I give my share of the purple carrots to my mother.

Now use what you learned to recognize cause and effect.

Answer the questions on the next page.

Practice the Skill 1

Practice recognizing cause and effect in the passage you just read.

EXAMPLE

Why does the narrator help Amir in the garden?

A He likes to water plants.

B He doesn't have a yard.

C Amir can't do all the work himself.

D Amir is too busy to water the plants.

Look for details about what happened in the story.

I see that the narrator helps Amir in the second paragraph. I look for details about why he helps Amir with his garden.

Find clue words near the event.

I see the word *so* which tells me that the narrator helping Amir is the effect.

Look for the event that makes this happen.

I see that Amir said that the garden is too much work for him to do by himself. This caused the narrator to help Amir.

Now read each question. Circle the letter of the best answer.

1. What will happen if the plants aren't watered every day?

    A Weeds will grow in the garden.

    B The carrots will not grow.

    C The plants will die.

    D Amir will be unhappy.

2. Why does Amir give the narrator carrots?

    A Amir doesn't like carrots.

    B Amir can't sell the carrots.

    C The narrator helps with the garden.

    D The garden belongs to the narrator.

3. Because the narrator's friend said the purple carrots were really weird —

    A everybody had seconds

    B nobody came to school

    C nobody ate lunch

    D nobody would eat them

4. What happened when the narrator ate too many carrots?

    A He felt sick.

    B He felt tired.

    C He got a cold.

    D He wanted more.

PHILADELPHIA SCHOOLS SAY "NO" TO SODA

Sodas are a thing of the past for Philadelphia schools.

PHILADELPHIA, PA—Students looking for soft drinks are out of luck. Philadelphia has **banned** the sale of sodas in schools. All the city's schools will now stock their vending machines with fruit juice, water, and milk instead.

The ban was made to help students get healthy. "There is not a good reason for soda to be sold in schools," said **nutrition** expert Sandy Sherman. Her group, The Food Trust, supported the ban. Sherman said that drinking too much soda can result in diabetes and cavities. It can even stop children from drinking milk.

Philadelphia has about 214,000 students. It is the second major U.S. city to enforce a ban on soda. In 2003, New York school districts banned not just soda but candy and sugary snacks as well. But Philadelphia's teachers' lounges will continue to sell the outlawed beverages.

Write About It

Use the graphic organizer below to identify cause and effect. Ask yourself why the schools stopped serving soda. Write why that happened in the "Cause" box.

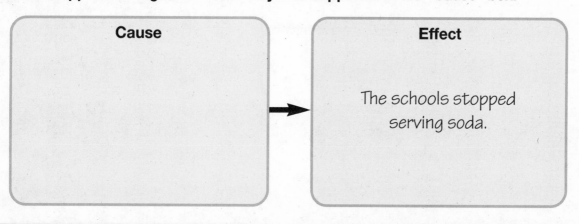

Cause

Effect

The schools stopped serving soda.

Review

You have learned how to **recognize cause and effect**. A **cause** is an event that makes something happen. The **effect** is what happens as a result.

Review the steps to recognize cause and effect.

- Read to find out what happens in the story.
- Think about what happened. Ask yourself, "Why did this happen?"
- Look for clue words, such as *so, therefore, as a result, because,* and *since.*

Practice 1

Read the following passage. As you read, think about what happened. Then think about why it happened. Look for clue words to help you find the cause and effect.

> My best friend Samantha wanted to surprise me on my birthday. As a result, she didn't call before coming to my house. The only problem was that I wasn't at my house. She had to wait for two hours before I came home.

Fill in the chart below to identify the cause and effect in the passage.

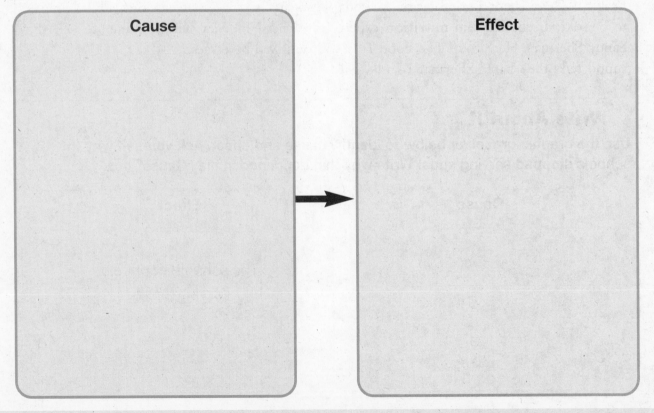

Cause

Effect

Practice 2

Read the passage. Look for cause and effect.

Most people wear light clothing when running a marathon because they can go faster. At a marathon in Scotland, Lloyd Scott had a different idea. Scott wore a deep-sea diving suit that caused him to run *slowly*. The suit weighed over 130 pounds, so he couldn't run very fast at all. It took him six days, four hours, 30 minutes, and 56 seconds before he finished. You're probably wondering why anyone would do this. Scott ran in the suit to raise money for charity! Next time he's going to run in an even heavier suit of armor.

Fill in this graphic organizer to recognize causes and effects in the passage.

Cause	Effect

Practice 3

Read the passage. Use clue words to recognize causes and effects. Then answer the questions. Make a graphic organizer on a separate sheet of paper to organize your thoughts.

> Italy has a famous fountain called the Trevi Fountain. It is in the capital city, Rome. Since the fountain was carved in stone and has many details, it took more than thirty years to complete.
>
> At the center of the fountain is a huge statue of Neptune, the Roman god of the sea. To his left and right are two powerful horses. One is angry and wild. It stands for stormy seas. The other is gentle and tame. It stands for peaceful seas. Today, many people come from far away to visit the fountain because they have seen it in famous movies.
>
> Many people throw coins into the fountain and make a wish. They believe that if you throw a coin into the fountain, then your wish will come true.

1. Why did the fountain take more than thirty years to build?

   _____

   _____

2. Why do people come from around the world to see the fountain?

   _____

   _____

3. Why do people throw coins into the fountain?

   _____

   _____

Guided Instruction 2

To **recognize cause and effect** you look for events and why they happen. A **cause** makes something happen. The **effect** is what happens as a result of the cause.

As you saw on pages 41–43, graphic organizers help readers recognize cause and effect.

- In the first box write the cause.
- In the second box write the effect.

Here's How

Read these sentences. Think about why things happen. What cause and effect do you recognize?

Deserts stretch across Australia's middle region. There is very little water, so the land is very dry and sandy. During the summer, it gets very hot.

Think About It

Cause		Effect
There is very little water.	→	The land is very dry.

Predict

When you **predict,** you look for clues about a passage and make a guess about what you will read.

- Read the title and look at any pictures to get an idea of what the passage might be about.
- As you read each paragraph, predict what you will read next.
- Check whether your predictions were correct and change them as you read on.

Read the story. Use the Reading Guide for tips that can help you predict and recognize cause and effect.

Reading Guide

Read the title. What do you think the passage will be about?

Why did so many people move to Coober Pedy?

Does the clue word since tell you that something is a cause or an effect?

One COOL Town

Australia is a big country. People say it is "down under." That's because it lies below the equator. On the coast, the **climate** is warm and gentle. There is plenty of water. Deserts stretch across Australia's middle region. There is very little water, so the land is very dry and sandy. During the summer, it gets very hot.

One special town lies in that hot, dry place. It's called Coober Pedy. People went to Coober Pedy because a boy named Will Hutchinson once found treasure there! In 1915, Will found opals in the rocks under the sand. Opals are gems. They are rare and very **precious.** People searched for opals so they could become rich.

At first, people built normal homes and stores. But their homes were uncomfortable because of the heat. Then someone built an underground house! Outside, it was 140 degrees. Inside the house, it was 70 degrees. Since it was so much cooler underground, many people copied the house. Meanwhile, the opal mines were a huge success. As a result, the town grew.

Today, more than three thousand people live there. Most of them live in underground homes. They have real rooms and full kitchens. They have televisions and computers. Coober Pedy has underground stores, too. Kids swim in an underground pool. Guests stay at underground hotels. Coober Pedy is a very "cool" town.

Coober Pedy

Answer the questions on the next page.

Practice the Skill 2

Practice recognizing cause and effect by answering questions about the story you just read. Read each question. Circle the letter of the best answer.

1. Why do people say that Australia is "down under"?

   A There are opal mines under the sand.

   B The country is below the equator.

   C Some people live underground.

   D A desert stretches across the middle.

2. Why did many people move to Coober Pedy?

   A They heard there was water there.

   B They wanted to live in a desert.

   C They wanted to build underground homes.

   D They heard about the boy's discovery of opals.

3. Why did people want the opals?

   A so they could become rich

   B so they could live underground

   C so they could explore the rocks

   D so they could move to town

4. Why were the first homes in Coober Pedy uncomfortable?

   A They were full of sand.

   B They had no computers.

   C It was too hot inside them.

   D It was too cool inside them.

5. Because the opal mines were a huge success, —

   A people moved underground

   B Coober Pedy grew larger

   C the mines ran out of opals

   D people bought televisions

6. On a separate sheet of paper, explain why Coober Pedy is a "cool" town.

IT'S A COCOA-TASTROPHE!

Containers filled with cocoa beans have sunk to the bottom of Brooklyn's East River.

NEW YORK, NY—It might have turned into a scene from "Willy Wonka and the Chocolate Factory." At least 800,000 pounds of cocoa beans were accidentally dropped into Brooklyn's East River. The boat was docked at Brooklyn Marine Terminal on its way to a factory in Chicago owned by Blommer Chocolate. About 600,000 dollars worth of cocoa beans were lost as a result of the accident.

No one is sure what caused the accident. The boat carrying the cocoa began to wobble. The containers slid off into the river. Then, the boat itself sank. No one was hurt in the accident. Since the cocoa beans were stored in sealed containers, no cocoa beans mixed with the water.

Experts don't expect the containers to break, so the cocoa will probably never end up in the water. The containers will just sit at the bottom of the river. Even if the containers do break open, experts don't believe that the cocoa beans will pose any threat to **marine** wildlife.

Write About It

Now you will practice the skill using a real news story. On a separate sheet of paper, describe what happened to the cocoa beans and what caused this to happen.

Read this article about a famous pirate. Then answer the questions on the next page.

THE STORY OF CAPTAIN KIDD

William Kidd started his career as a British sailor, but he ended it as one of the most famous pirates in history. As a young sailor, Kidd worked on ships that attacked England's enemies. Kidd **plundered** and stole from French ships because they were at war with England.

Since he was a good sailor, he was given his own ship to command. It was called the "Adventure Galley." England was at war, so they built a ship with 34 cannons that would be powerful. Kidd was told to attack only French ships.

Kidd wanted only the best men working on his ship. That is why he went to New York City to **recruit** them himself. He found men that were mean and tough. They were also good sailors. In 1696, they set sail to attack French ships. Anything they could steal from these ships they could keep. Most of the men wanted to be on the ship for one reason: treasure. They hungered for riches, and this was their chance.

For months, they did not come across any enemy ships. Since they attacked no ships, they took no **booty.** Soon, Kidd's crew became angry because they weren't getting rich. Kidd feared a **mutiny.** As a result, he attacked any ship he found. He didn't care if they were enemies of England or not. In a short time, they attacked many ships and took a lot of treasure.

When they returned to New York City, Kidd was arrested for piracy. He was a pirate because he attacked ships that weren't enemies of England. He was sent to England for trial and was found guilty. Then, he was hanged. No one knows what happened to the treasures he stole. Even today, there are those who believe his treasure is buried somewhere, waiting to be found.

Read each question. Circle the letter of the best answer.

1. Why was Kidd supposed to attack only French ships?

   A French ships carried treasures.

   B France had the toughest pirates.

   C France was at war with England.

   D France was Kidd's homeland.

2. Kidd was given his own ship to command because he —

   A bought his own ship

   B was a New Yorker

   C was a British citizen

   D was a good sailor

3. Why did England build the "Adventure Galley" with 34 cannons?

   A All ships had cannons.

   B England was at war.

   C Kidd asked for cannons.

   D France wanted the ship.

4. Why did Kidd recruit his own crew in New York City?

   A He wanted the best men on his ship.

   B He didn't want the British on his ship.

   C His crew was too mean and too tough.

   D His ship was built for Americans.

5. What happened because they attacked no ships?

   A They took no booty.

   B They were all fired.

   C The war ended.

   D Kidd got arrested.

6. Why did Kidd's crew become angry?

   A Kidd became a pirate.

   B Their ship was too small.

   C Sailing was too much work.

   D They weren't getting rich.

7. What did Kidd do that made him a pirate?

   A He attacked ships that were French.

   B He attacked ships that weren't enemies.

   C He attacked ships in New York.

   D He attacked ships that had no booty.

8. On a separate sheet of paper, explain why Kidd became a pirate.

Show What You Know

Before you begin this lesson, take this quiz to show what you know about using context clues. Read this story about a boy and his neighbor. Then answer the questions.

After School with Mrs. Lin

When my little brother José started school this year, my mom went back to work. I'm in fourth grade now. I told Mom I could be in charge until she came home from work. I'm <u>mature</u> and grown-up enough to watch my brother. Mom didn't agree.

She called our neighbor, Mrs. Lin, and asked her to watch us. At first, I was upset. Mrs. Lin is kind of old. I thought afternoons with her would be boring. I was really wrong!

When we came home from school, Mrs. Lin had chips and fruit salsa for us. We were so hungry that we <u>devoured</u> everything in about five minutes. We ate everything in sight! Then, Mrs. Lin let José and me use our skateboards. We showed her some tricks we've been practicing. She laughed and clapped her hands at every stunt we performed. She even tried riding my skateboard herself. I never thought she'd be able to stay up, but she did. It was great!

By the time Mom came home that evening, we were <u>exhausted</u>. She said she hadn't seen us that tired in a long time!

Circle the letter of the best answer.

1. What does the word <u>mature</u> mean?

   A excited
   B grown-up
   C boring
   D fun

2. The word <u>devoured</u> means —

   A played
   B drank
   C looked
   D ate

3. The word <u>tricks</u> is a context clue for —

   A exhausted
   B boring
   C stunt
   D devoured

4. What word means the same as <u>exhausted</u>?

   A tired
   B bored
   C hungry
   D great

Introduction

Context clues are words that help you figure out the meaning of a new word.

To use context clues,

- Read the sentence with the new word. See if you can tell what it means.
- Look at sentences that come before and after the new word. Look for clues to the word's meaning.
- When you think you know the meaning, try using it in place of the new word.

Here's How

Read these sentences. Use context clues to figure out the meaning of the word <u>treks</u>.

As a child, Ms. Scott spent lots of time outdoors. Her dad took her on long <u>treks</u>. They would go on many hikes through the woods. Sometimes, they even stayed overnight in tents.

Think About It

1. I *see the unfamiliar word* <u>treks</u> *written in the paragraph above.*

2. I *look at the next sentence and read that they* go on many hikes through the woods. *I know that a hike is a long walk.*

3. I *think the word* <u>treks</u> *means "hikes."*

Monitor and Clarify

When you **monitor and clarify,** you check to make sure that you understand what you are reading.

- After reading each section, pause and try to restate the main ideas.
- If you did not understand the main ideas, reread the section.
- As you reread each sentence, try to put the ideas into your own words to help you understand.

Read this passage. Use the Reading Guide for tips that can help you monitor and clarify and use context clues as you read.

Reading Guide

Look at the sentence before and after the word <u>terrain</u> to find the meaning.

Find context clues to figure out what <u>encounter</u> means.

Check this paragraph to make sure you understand the events. Reread each sentence and try and retell them in your own words.

Look at What That Kea Did!

My teacher is Ms. Scott. She was raised in New Zealand, a nation in the South Pacific. She has shared many stories with us about growing up there.

Ms. Scott used to own a horse. It was easier to travel on the bumpy <u>terrain</u> that way. The land wasn't developed, and the roads weren't paved.

As a child, Ms. Scott spent lots of time outdoors. Her dad took her on long <u>treks</u>. They would go on many hikes through the woods. Sometimes, they even stayed overnight in tents.

One time they came across a kea, a wild parrot with red feathers. It was an interesting <u>encounter</u>, to say the least. Keas aren't afraid of people and they like to steal things. Their strong beaks can get into just about anything.

Ms. Scott and her dad had gone hiking after putting up their tent. When they returned, the tent was <u>demolished</u>. It was just a pile of torn canvas. The food was all eaten. At first, they were nervous. Then, they saw the <u>evidence</u>—a heap of feathers! That was all the proof they needed to blame the kea.

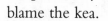

Now use what you learned to use context clues.

Answer the questions on the next page.

Practice using context clues about the passage you just read.

EXAMPLE

What is the meaning of the word <u>terrain</u>?

A horse

B land

C camp

D bird

Read the sentence with the new word.

<u>Terrain</u> is an unfamiliar word to me.

Look for context clues that suggest the meaning of the word.

The word <u>terrain</u> is followed by a sentence that contains the context clue *land*.

Replace the word with a familiar word and check to see if it makes sense.

If I replace the word <u>terrain</u> with the word *land*, the sentence makes sense and I understand what it means.

Now read each question. Circle the letter of the best answer.

1. The phrase <u>came across</u> helps the reader understand the meaning of the word —

   A demolished

   B evidence

   C encounter

   D treks

2. Which context clue gives a meaning to the word <u>demolished</u>?

   A a pile of torn canvas

   B blame the kea

   C they were nervous

   D like to steal things

3. What does the word <u>demolished</u> mean?

   A eaten

   B missing

   C vanished

   D destroyed

4. What word means the same as <u>evidence</u>?

   A beak

   B land

   C proof

   D tent

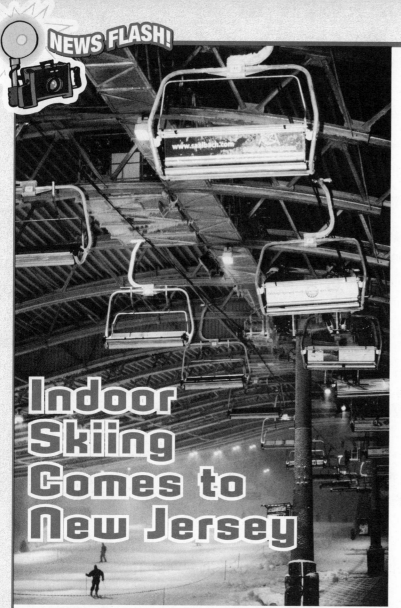

Indoor Skiing Comes to New Jersey

New Jersey will soon be home to an indoor ski center.

EAST RUTHERFORD, NJ— An indoor ski center is expected to open in New Jersey. The Snow Dome is being built at the Meadowlands in East Rutherford.

This will be the first indoor ski center to open in the United States. There are about 50 other indoor ski centers in the world, including several in Japan, Germany, and China.

It was hard work to make this project happen. It took over a year to make the deal to <u>construct</u> the indoor mountain. Now the workers will start building. Visitors can start skiing in 2007.

The Meadowlands is a sports and entertainment center. It is home to the New York Giants. There is also a multi-sport arena and racetrack. The Snow Dome is going to be part of a new addition. The 5-million-square-foot center will also have outdoor rides, fashion shows, and the world's largest movie theater.

Write About It

Use this graphic organizer to find the meaning of the word <u>construct</u>. Decide which sentence helps you understand the meaning.

Sentence Before New Word	Sentence With New Word	Sentence After New Word	Meaning
It was hard work to make this project happen.			

Ladder to Success

Review

As you read, you can **use context clues** to figure out the meaning of new words.

Review the steps you can take to use context clues.

- Read the sentence or paragraph with the unfamiliar word.
- Look for words that may provide clues about the meaning of the unfamiliar word.
- Replace the unfamiliar word with a word that you know and check to see if the sentence makes sense.

Practice 1

Read the following passage. As you read, look for context clues that can help you understand the meaning of unfamiliar words. Replace any unfamiliar words with words that you know and check to see if the sentence or paragraph makes sense.

> I can't wait for our school's lip-sync contest next Friday! <u>Contestants</u> select their own songs for the performance. Lots of students are participating, and even some teachers! Some people are dressing up like the original singers. I'm going to lip-sync to an old Elvis tune. Wait until the crowd sees my costume!

Using the context clues from the passage, fill in each part of this diagram.

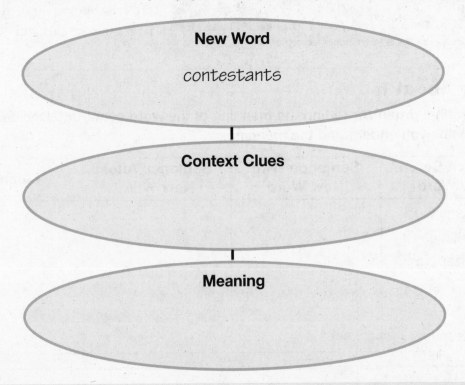

New Word

contestants

Context Clues

Meaning

Practice 2

Read the passage. What context clues help you understand the meaning of the underlined words?

A boy named Chester Greenwood really wanted to go skating one day in 1873. Although the temperature was below freezing, he braved it.

He didn't skate for very long. His ears quickly turned numb and bright red. When they started throbbing, he feared they would fall off! Chester <u>sprinted</u> home. He ran as fast as he could to ask his grandmother for help.

Together, they found a solution. First, they cut circles out of fur and velvet and sewed them together. Then, they sewed each circle to the end of a <u>flexible</u> piece of wire. The wire could bend to fit around Chester's head.

The next day, Chester went skating again. This time, he stayed outside for hours and his ears didn't freeze. He was happy with his invention—earmuffs!

Use this graphic organizer to find the meanings of the two underlined words.

New Word	Context Clues	Meaning

Practice 3

Read this passage about eyes. Use context clues and what you already know about eyes to figure out the meanings of new words. Then answer the questions. Make a graphic organizer on a separate sheet of paper to organize your thoughts.

Have you ever looked in a mirror to examine your eyes? If so, you're only looking at a small part. They're actually the size of ping-pong balls!

The iris is the colored area of your eye. The black dot in the middle is called the pupil. The iris has strong muscles that protect the pupil. When light enters, the iris <u>adjusts</u>. It changes in size to let in the right amount of light.

Eyelids guard the front of your eyes. They keep them clean and moist. They also protect the eyes by blinking. Your eyelids have incredible <u>reflexes</u>. You notice a quick reaction if light shines too brightly or wind blows strongly. The eyelids will close very quickly. Your eyelashes keep the <u>grime</u> out of your eyes. Nobody likes dirt in their eyes.

Eyes have their own watering system, too! When you blink, a small tear forms in your tear duct. The tear washes away germs and dust. It also keeps your eye from drying out. As you can see, your eyes are pretty amazing!

1. What context clues can help readers figure out the meaning of the word <u>adjusts</u>? What does the word mean?

_____

_____

2. What does the word <u>reflexes</u> mean?

_____

_____

3. Based on the context clues, what is the meaning of the word <u>grime</u>?

_____

_____

Introduction

A **context clue** is a word or phrase that readers can use to figure out the meanings of new words. **Using context clues** can help you understand and enjoy what you read. It will also help you learn the meanings of many new words.

As you saw on pages 55–57, a context clue chart can help readers use context clues.

- In the first box, write the unfamiliar word.
- In the second box, write any clue words that can help you understand the unfamiliar word. These might be definitions, examples, or phrases that explain the difficult word.
- In the third box, write your own definition of the unfamiliar word.

Here's How

Read these sentences about Uncle Joe's Pizzeria. Look for context clues to learn the meaning of the word <u>bustling</u>.

He owns a popular pizzeria. It's the busiest pizza shop in the whole town. It's always <u>bustling</u> with customers.

Think About It

New Word	Context Clues	Meaning
bustling	popular, busiest, customers	The word *bustling* means "busy."

Try This Strategy

Visualize

When you **visualize,** you make a picture in your mind of what you are reading.

- As you read, develop a detailed picture in your mind of the setting, people, and action.
- When you read an unfamiliar word, picture the scene in your mind.
- Reread the sentence again and think of a meaning for the unfamiliar word that would make sense in the scene you created in your mind.

Read the passage. Use the Reading Guide for tips that can help you visualize and use context clues as you read.

Reading Guide

What clue words tell you what it is like inside Uncle Joe's restaurant?

What context clues help you understand the word <u>abundant</u>?

How does visualizing help you understand the meaning of <u>orderly</u>?

Uncle Joe's Pizzeria

Last year, I spent summer vacation helping out at Uncle Joe's restaurant. He owns a popular pizzeria. It's the busiest pizza shop in the whole town. It's always <u>bustling</u> with customers.

Uncle Joe knew he could count on me because I'm so <u>reliable</u>. He gave me plenty of <u>tasks</u>. Luckily, I like all the jobs in the pizza shop. Each morning, I started by helping the chefs prepare food. First, I had to divide the pizza dough into small, rolled-up sections. After I rolled it, I put it on wax paper with flour and covered it. Next, I had to slice up pizza toppings. My uncle's restaurant offers an <u>abundant</u> choice of toppings. Because there are so many kinds of toppings, it always took me a long time to slice everything up.

Once the customers arrived, I had to make sure the tables stayed clean and the restaurant looked <u>orderly</u>. Uncle Joe always told me a disorganized restaurant was a sign of bad customer service.

At the end of each day, I helped Uncle Joe clean up. I took out the garbage, mopped the floor, and put away extra food.

Working at a restaurant sure is tiring. Even though I was so tired, I was <u>satisfied</u>. I felt really happy about my work at the pizzeria.

Answer the questions on the next page.

Practice using context clues by answering questions about the passage you just read. Read each question. Circle the letter of the best answer.

1. What words from the passage mean the same as <u>tasks</u>?

   A customers

   B tables

   C toppings

   D jobs

2. Which phrase provides a clue to the meaning of the word <u>reliable</u>?

   A bustling with customers

   B he could count on me

   C I started in the kitchen

   D plenty of jobs to do

3. What context clue helps identify the meaning of <u>abundant</u>?

   A slice up

   B long time

   C many kinds

   D covered it

4. Which word means the opposite of <u>orderly</u>?

   A disorganized

   B popular

   C reliable

   D service

5. What does the word <u>satisfied</u> mean?

   A tired

   B happy

   C bored

   D clean

6. Choose two of the underlined words in the passage. Use them in sentences on a separate sheet of paper to show you understand the meaning of each word.

Fossett set the record for the longest nonstop solo flight.

FOSSETT SOARS TO ANOTHER RECORD

CAPE CANAVERAL, FL—Adventurer Steve Fossett has made history again. The American aviator broke the record for the world's longest, nonstop flight. Fossett flew his plane, the Virgin Atlantic GlobalFlyer, almost 27,000 miles without stopping.

Fossett, who was the first person to fly around the world solo, started his record-setting trip from the Kennedy Space Center. He flew over the United States, parts of South America, China, and Japan. He also crossed the Pacific Ocean and traveled across the Atlantic Ocean twice.

His trip was not always smooth sailing, however. Along the way, his plane hit two birds, had a fuel leak, and was forced to fly through harsh winds. In the end, it was not enough to deter Fossett from his goal. Nothing would prevent him from finishing. He completed the historic flight in three and a half days.

This was the seventh record Fossett has set with this plane. He also has his name in the record books for sailing, skiing, swimming, ballooning, and car racing events. Fossett has set 109 world records so far. The 61-year-old daredevil shows no signs of stopping any time soon.

Write About It

Reread the underlined sentence in the article. What does <u>deter</u> mean in this sentence? What clues in that paragraph helped you to find the meaning?

Read this article about a forest. Then answer the questions on the next page.

MUIR WOODS

Deep woods once stretched along the west coast of the United States. Towering evergreen trees grew there. Some of these tall trees were redwoods. Others were firs. Today, most of them have been cut down. The wood was used to build homes. The land was cleared for cities and towns. One small forest of tall trees remains. It is deep and dark there. The tall trees stretch up to the sky. They stand on a floor of soft green moss. The only sounds are songs of birds and the splashing of streams. It's a quiet, calm place, quite different from the commotion of its busy neighbor, the big city of San Francisco. This forest is called Muir Woods.

At first, the forest was saved because of its remote location. It was far from any town, hidden in a deep canyon. People knew it would be hard to chop down the trees and carry them up the steep cliffs. So they cut other trees in flat areas. They left that forest alone.

Then people made a new city, San Francisco. It grew very fast. Builders needed more supplies. It seemed a good time to cut those trees in the canyon. Luckily, William Kent saved them. He bought the whole forest. Then he went to President Theodore Roosevelt. Kent promised to give the forest to our country if laws would preserve it. Roosevelt agreed

to save the forest. He wanted to name it Kent Woods, but Kent said no. He wanted it named for John Muir. Muir was a great conservationist. He worked hard to save many of our woods, mountains, and wild areas.

Today, laws protect acres and acres of wild lands. Like Muir Woods, those lands belong to the wild animals that have always lived there—squirrels, birds, bears, and wolves. They also belong to the people of the United States.

Read each question. Circle the letter of the best answer.

1. What does the word <u>towering</u> mean?

   A tall

   B dark

   C green

   D soft

2. What is the opposite of <u>commotion</u>?

   A noise

   B song

   C dark

   D peace

3. Which phrase gives a clue to the meaning of <u>remote</u>?

   A hard to chop down

   B far from any town

   C quite different from

   D trees in flat areas

4. What means the same as <u>steep</u>?

   A rising

   B flat

   C tall

   D short

5. What means the opposite of <u>preserve</u>?

   A build

   B save

   C destroy

   D make

6. Which sentence helps define the word <u>preserve</u>?

   A He wanted to name it Kent Woods.

   B Muir was a great conservationist.

   C Roosevelt agreed to save the forest.

   D Then people made a new city.

7. Based on details in the passage, what is a <u>conservationist</u>?

   A a person who buys wild lands

   B a person who saves wild lands

   C a person who helps cities grow

   D a person who makes laws

8. Find the unfamiliar words in the passage. On a separate sheet of paper use each one in a sentence that gives a fact about Muir Woods.

Show What You Know

Before you begin this lesson, take this quiz to show what you know about main ideas and details. Read this story about a boy's thoughts about food. Then answer the questions.

Picky, Picky!

I'm a picky eater. I don't like sour cream. It's too slimy! Most of all, though, I don't like gooey things. Once Grandma put a raw clam on my plate. It looked like a puddle of glue.

Mom often puts two great things on my plate, like chicken and rice. Then she'll add something new. Once, she added an artichoke. "What's this?" I asked. "A giant flower bud from Mars?" I kid around with her, but I know she's trying to help. She wants me to try new things.

To help me try new things, Dad plays "What If?" He thinks about a weird-looking food that many people love to eat. Then he asks me, "What if you were the first person to see it?" The point is that if no one ever tried it, we wouldn't know about that yummy food!

We've discussed many great foods in that game. For instance, lots of people love lobster. It's a really weird-looking animal, though. It looks like a giant bug. What if you were the first person to see a lobster? Would you be brave enough to eat it? Not me! But I do love lobster, so I'm grateful to the really brave person who took that first bite.

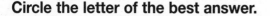

Circle the letter of the best answer.

1. This story is mostly about —

   A a game Dad plays

   B a boy who doesn't like to try new foods

   C different kinds of food that are slimy

   D strange-looking foods

2. Which detail from the story is best connected to the main idea of the story?

   A Mom puts chicken and rice on the boy's plate.

   B The boy knows his mom is trying to help.

   C The boy does not like gooey things.

   D Lots of people love lobster.

3. What is the main idea of the first paragraph?

   A I'm a picky eater.

   B I don't like sour cream.

   C Most of all, I don't like gooey things.

   D Raw clams look like puddles of glue.

4. What new detail might be added to the story to support the main idea?

   A different ways to cook lobster

   B examples of places where lobsters live

   C other foods that the narrator doesn't like

   D another game that Dad likes to play

Introduction

The **main idea** is the most important idea or event in a passage or a paragraph. The **details** are smaller ideas that tell more about the main idea. You can **identify main ideas and details** by finding the important ideas and the details that support them.

To identify main ideas and details,

- Read the passage or paragraph. Think about what it is mostly about.
- Find the main idea. The main idea of a passage is often in the first or last paragraph. The main idea of a paragraph is often in the first sentence.
- Look for details that tell about the main idea. They might answer *who? what? where? when?* and *why?*

Here's How

Read these sentences. What is the main idea?

At Spence Farm, each horse enjoys the comforts of its own stall. It sleeps there at night, safe and warm. It is fed grain there.

Think About It

1. The passage is mostly about how the horses live at Spence Farm.

2. The first sentence tells the main idea. The main idea is that the horses are comfortable at Spence Farm.

3. The other sentences tell more about the comforts of Spence Farm. I know that the main idea I chose is correct.

Try This Strategy

Scan and Skim

When you **scan and skim,** you look over a passage before reading to get an idea of what it will be about.

- Read the title and look at any pictures. Think about what the passage might be about.
- Skim the passage, looking for key words. What do you think the main idea is?

Read this passage. Use the Reading Guide for tips that can help you to scan and skim and identify main ideas and details.

Reading Guide

Scan and skim the passage. Think of what the passage is mainly about. Look for clues in the title and picture.

This paragraph tells many things the horses do. Think of a main idea these details support.

Look at the details the writer gives in the passage. Think of a main idea they tell more about.

A Great Place for Old Horses

Our class went on a field trip to Spence Farm. About fifty horses live there. They don't work or give people rides. No one asks these horses to do anything but have fun. Spence Farm is like a **retirement** home for horses!

At Spence Farm, each horse enjoys the comforts of its own stall. It sleeps there at night, safe and warm. It is fed grain there. Each morning, it is brushed. Then it is led out to the big fenced meadow.

In the meadow, the horses have lots of leisure time. They need this quiet time to feel strong. They nibble on the grass. Sometimes they trot around, feeling the fresh air.

The horses like to have their fun, too. They act friendly towards each other. Sometimes they play games, like "follow the leader."

These old horses come to Spence Farm from many places. Some come from the circus. Others worked with the police. Still others worked in rodeos. After all that work, they deserve a break!

Now use what you learned to identify main ideas and details.

Answer the questions on the next page.

Practice the Skill 1

Practice identifying main ideas and details in the passage you just read.

EXAMPLE

What main idea does the detail "Some come from the circus" support?

A Some horses worked with the police.

B Spence Farm is a retirement home for horses.

C The horses come from many places.

D Some horses worked in rodeos.

Read the last paragraph to find what it is mainly about.

The detail is mainly about where the horses come from.

Decide on the main idea of the paragraph.

The main idea is that horses come from many places.

Look for details that tell more about the main idea.

The other sentences in the paragraph tell more about places the horses came from. I know that the main idea I chose is correct.

Now read each question. Circle the letter of the best answer.

1. From the title, you might guess that the article's main idea is —

   A what old horses eat

   B a place where old horses live

   C the average age that old horses reach

   D great old horses

2. Which sentence tells the main idea of the first paragraph?

   A Our class went on a field trip to Spence Farm.

   B About fifty horses live there.

   C They don't work or give people rides.

   D Spence Farm is like a retirement home for horses!

3. Which detail tells why the horses have lots of leisure time in the meadow?

   A They don't work or give people rides.

   B They need this quiet time to feel strong.

   C They nibble on the grass.

   D Sometimes they trot around, feeling the fresh air.

4. What is the main idea of the fourth paragraph?

   A Spence Farm is for old horses.

   B The horses like to have their fun.

   C The horses act friendly with each other.

   D Sometimes the horses play games.

TOWN TO CELEBRATE ANNUAL RAIN DAY

Waynesburg, Pennsylvania, celebrates its annual Rain Day.

WAYNESBURG, PA—So much for rain ruining holidays! The town of Waynesburg will celebrate "Rain Day" on July 29th. People in the town have been observing this holiday for more than 130 years.

Events this year will include singing, dancing, umbrella decorating, and the Miss Rain Day Contest. The biggest event will be the annual bet. Every year the mayor bets his hat that it will rain on July 29th. The Mayor makes his bet against an actor, athlete, or other celebrity. This year, Waynesburg hopes to add billionaire Donald Trump's hat to its collection.

Rain has fallen on July 29th in 109 of the last 130 years. This strange weather pattern was discovered by a local farmer. He noticed that it would always rain on July 29th, his birthday. Word soon spread and before long, the town began holding the annual rainy day event.

Write About It

Now you will practice the skill using a real news story. Complete this graphic organizer by filling in the details of this article.

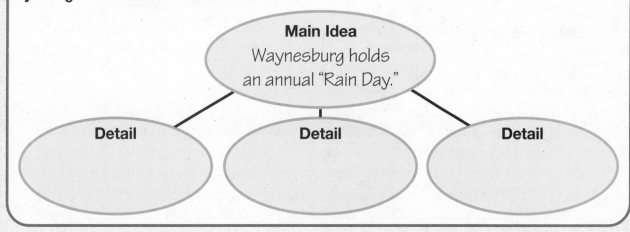

Main Idea
Waynesburg holds an annual "Rain Day."

Detail

Detail

Detail

Ladder to Success

Review

As you read, you can **identify main ideas and details** in a passage. You can look for the most important ideas in a passage. Then you can search for facts or events that support it.

Review the steps you can use to identify main ideas and details.

- As you read, think about what the paragraph or passage is mainly about.
- Look for the main idea. The main idea of a passage is sometimes in the first or last paragraph. The main idea of a paragraph is sometimes in the first or last sentence.
- Find details that support the main idea. These are smaller ideas or events. They might answer questions such as *who, what, when, where,* and *why* about the main idea.

Practice 1

Read the following passage. As you read, look for a sentence that tells what the passage is about. Then look for details that give information about the main idea.

Some forest fires are very helpful. They clear the forest of old, dead trees and harmful weeds. They also let sunlight enter the forest, helping new plants grow. Fire can even help some plants, like the jack pine tree. Its seeds are held in cones that are sealed shut. In a fire, the cones open and the seeds drop to the ground. After the fire, new jack pines begin to grow.

Now identify the main idea and important details. Use this graphic organizer.

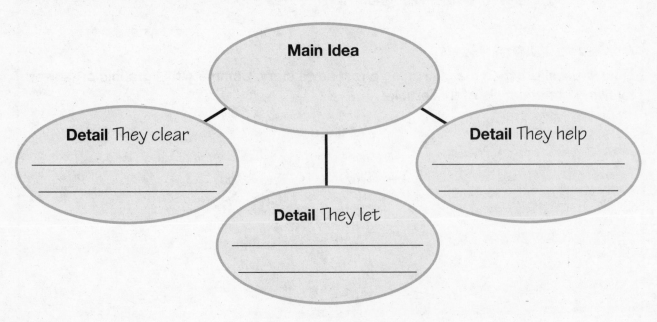

Practice 2

Read this passage. In each paragraph, look for a sentence that tells the main idea. It might be the first sentence, or it might be the last sentence. Then look for sentences that answer *who, what, when, where,* and *why* questions about the main idea.

> This summer, Mom started a new club. She wanted to give kids something fun to do after school. We cook, have nature walks, and even make crafts.
>
> One member of the club, Tanya, is always asking questions. One day, Mom suggested we make corn bread, and Tanya asked why. Another day we walked through the woods and tried to **identify** different leaves. Tanya asked why we should do that. Mom was always ready with the answer.
>
> I am amazed at Mom's patience. She told me that raising children can teach you a lot of patience. She also said she likes it when kids ask questions. "When kids ask questions, it means they want to learn," she says.

Fill in the ovals to identify the main ideas and details in the second paragraph of this passage.

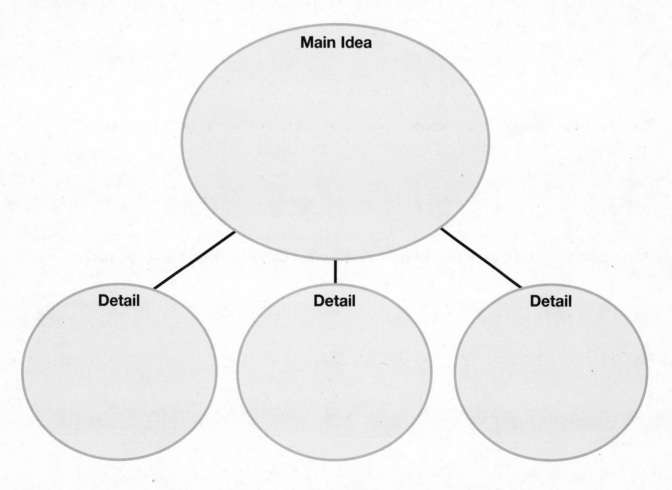

Practice 3

Read this passage. Then answer the questions. Make a graphic organizer on a separate sheet of paper to organize your thoughts.

A team of doctors wanted to find a new way to get kids to exercise. They knew that kids spend a lot of time sitting at school. So the doctors made a plan to bring exercise to the classroom.

The doctors took away the kids' chairs. They wanted students to move instead of sit. They knew that moving around burns calories, which helps people stay in shape. Then they gave each kid a laptop with a wireless Internet connection. They also wired each kid with a motion **sensor.**

The doctors told the kids to move. The sensors showed which kids moved the most. As they moved, they also used their laptops to learn their school subjects.

After a few days, the kids took a quiz. The quiz showed that they learned their subjects well. The motion sensors showed that they burned calories, too. The experiment worked!

1. In your own words, tell what the main idea of this article is.

_____

_____

2. What detail tells *why* the doctors made a plan to bring exercise into the classroom?

_____

_____

3. What is the main idea of the last paragraph? What details support the main idea?

_____

_____

LADDERS to SUCCESS

LESSON

5

Identifying
Main Ideas and
Details

Guided Instruction 2

Introduction

The **main idea** is the most important idea in a passage or a paragraph. The main idea is supported by **details,** such as facts, examples, and smaller events.

As you saw on pages 69–71, graphic organizers can help readers identify main ideas and details.

- Think about what the passage or paragraph is mostly about.
- Decide on the main idea. This is the big idea of the passage or paragraph.
- Find details that support the main idea. They should be related to the main idea.

Here's How

Read these sentences about space. Look for the main idea. Then look for details that support the main idea.

Two years later, a person finally went into space. A Soviet man named Yuri Gagarin was the first to fly into space. An American, Alan Shepard, reached space soon after.

Think About It

Main Idea
People started going into space.

Detail
Soviet Yuri Gagarin went into space first.

Detail
American Alan Shepard went into space next.

Try This Strategy

Summarize

Here's another strategy you can use to find main ideas and details. When you **summarize,** you look back on what you have read. Then you express the main ideas in your own words.

- As you read each paragraph, think about the main idea. Try saying the main idea in your own words. Reread the paragraph if you have trouble.
- At the end of the passage, think about the main ideas. Use them to summarize the passage in your own words.

Read the passage. Stop after you read each paragraph. Use the Reading Guide for tips that can help you to summarize and identify main ideas and details.

Reading Guide

The main idea of the passage is sometimes found in the first paragraph. Think about what the main idea might be.

Think of what this paragraph is mainly about. The details should tell more about this main idea.

Summarize this paragraph about what the United States did.

Summarize what the passage was about in your own words. Use the main idea of each paragraph to help.

THE RACE FOR SPACE

Fifty years ago, the space race began. The race was between the world's most powerful countries, the United States and the Soviet Union. The goal was to be the first to reach outer space.

Both countries were working hard to send a **satellite** into space. The Soviets got there first. In 1957, they launched Sputnik, a round, shiny object that circled the Earth. All it did was make beeping noises, but it made Americans nervous. They thought that if the Soviets controlled space, they could become more powerful than the United States.

The United States worked hard to catch up. The first American satellite took off in 1958. A new agency called NASA was created that focused on getting people into space.

Two years later, a person finally went into space. A Soviet man named Yuri Gagarin was the first to fly into space. An American, Alan Shepard, reached space soon after.

All this time, the Soviets were leading the space race. In 1969, however, the United States did something the Soviets had never done. They sent a man to the moon. Many people said the United States had won the space race.

Answer the questions on the next page.

Practice identifying main ideas and details. Read each question. Circle the letter of the best answer.

1. What is this passage mainly about?

   A what happened in the space race

   B what the space race was

   C how the first satellite was launched

   D how a man was sent into space

2. What is the main idea of the second paragraph?

   A All Sputnik did was make beeping noises.

   B The United States worked hard to catch up.

   C The launch of Sputnik made Americans nervous.

   D The Soviets launched a satellite into space first.

3. What detail could be added to the second paragraph to support the main idea?

   A Next, the Soviets sent Sputnik 2 into space.

   B Sputnik orbited earth for 92 days.

   C President Eisenhower wanted to win the space race.

   D Many satellites have been sent into space since Sputnik.

4. What is the main idea of the last paragraph?

   A The United States won the space race by sending a man to the moon.

   B The Soviets were winning the space race.

   C Many people were excited by the moon landing.

   D Nobody else had ever been to the moon before.

5. What detail best supports the idea that the United States worked hard to catch up in the space race?

   A The launch of Sputnik made many Americans nervous.

   B Yuri Gagarin was the first person to reach space.

   C A new agency called NASA was created.

   D Many people said the United States had won the space race.

6. Look back at the whole passage. In your own words, write the main idea of the passage.

A $20 bill with a Del Monte® sticker printed on it sold for $25,300.

$20 "BANANA" BILL SELLS FOR $25,300

FORT WORTH, TEXAS—Sold! A $20 bill with a fruit sticker on it sold at an auction for $25,300. The 1996 bill features a green, yellow, and red Del Monte® banana sticker on the front. The sticker was put right onto the paper when the bill was printed. U.S. Treasury Department officials are not sure how the mistake happened.

The unusual bill was printed at a U.S. Treasury Department building in Fort Worth. In 2003, collector Daniel Wishnatsky bought the bill online. He paid $10,100 for it. "I've collected for probably seven years now and nothing comes close to the way people react to it," Wishnatsky said. "Their eyes pop out."

The bill was sold again in 2006 at an auction in Florida. By then, it had increased in value to $25,300. The newest owner did not want to be identified, said auction director Dustin Johnston.

The $20 bill is in near-perfect **condition,** and has become famous among money collectors. It has appeared on the cover of two money magazines.

Write About It

Read the third paragraph of the article. Write the main idea in your own words. Then write a detail that supports this main idea.

Show What You Learned

9-16-11

Read this article about a common food. Then answer the questions on the next page.

A Lunch with Many Names

Long ago in England, there was a man named John Montagu. His title was Fourth Earl of Sandwich. This man liked to play games with his friends. He would sit at a table and play games for hours and hours, and he hated stopping the game to eat dinner. He asked his cook to make him something that he could eat while he played. He didn't want to use silverware. He didn't want a dish that might spill, like soup. He just wanted something easy, something he could pick up and eat while he played.

To please Montagu, his cook took some meat and cheese and put them between two pieces of bread. Montagu was very pleased. He asked the cook what the name of this special food was. His cook thought a while before saying, "I will name this food after you. I'll call it *the sandwich!*" Just think—the cook might have given it the man's last name instead of his title. Then you might be eating a Montagu for lunch today!

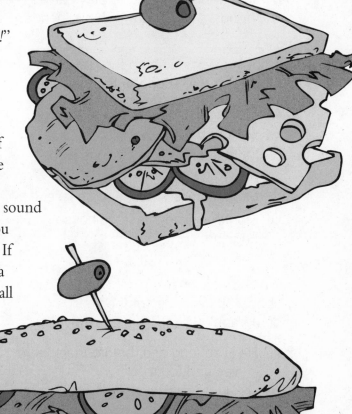

"Sandwich" is a strange name for this food, but it's not the only name. There is one kind of sandwich with many different names. It is made on a long roll. Inside it often has meats, cheese, lettuce, and tomatoes. Does that long sandwich sound familiar? What you call it depends on where you live. In Philadelphia, you might call it a hoagie. If you're from New Orleans, you probably call it a poor boy. If you live in New York, you might call it a hero. If you live in New England, chances are you call it a sub. That's short for "submarine," a name that describes its long shape. In other parts of the country, you might call it a grinder. This all seems very strange, indeed. It is, after all, the same sandwich!

Read each question. Circle the letter of the best answer.

1. What is this article mainly about?

   A the life of John Montagu

   B the name of a popular food

   C different types of sandwiches

   D the differences between sandwiches and soup

2. What is the main idea of the first paragraph?

   A John Montagu lived in England.

   B John Montagu wanted something that he could eat while playing games.

   C John Montagu did not like to eat soup.

   D John Montagu liked to play games for hours and hours with his friends.

3. What is one detail from the first paragraph that supports the main idea?

   A Montagu wanted to eat something without using silverware.

   B Montagu had many friends who played games.

   C Montagu liked meat and cheese.

   D Montagu lived in a large house in England.

4. Which detail answers a Why question about the main idea of the first paragraph?

   A He lived long ago, before there were knives and forks.

   B He didn't like the foods his cook usually made for him.

   C He didn't like to stop playing when it was time for dinner.

   D He didn't like to eat food while playing games.

5. What is the main idea of the third paragraph?

   A "Sandwich" is a strange name.

   B One kind of sandwich has many names.

   C There are many different kinds of sandwiches.

   D A hoagie is the same as a hero.

6. What detail best supports the main idea of the third paragraph?

   A "Sub" is short for "submarine."

   B The sandwiches all contain meat and cheese.

   C Many people live in New York and Philadelphia.

   D In New York, a sandwich is called a hero.

7. What do the pictures suggest the passage is about?

   A the names of a lunch food

   B different kinds of sandwiches

   C the importance of lunch

   D peoples' names

8. Write the main idea of the second paragraph in your own words.

78

Show What You Know

Before you begin this lesson, take this quiz to show what you know about drawing conclusions. Read this story about a winter vacation. Then answer the questions.

WINTER SPORTS FUN

My brother Mike goes to school in Colorado. It snows a lot there! Mike skis all winter long. Our home is in Tucson. There's no skiing here. When I visited Mike last winter, I had a great time learning to ski.

At first, I was wobbly on skis. The snow was slippery. I fell down a lot. So did everyone in my class. The instructor taught us the basic moves, and even how to get up after falling. Soon, I was whizzing downhill.

My skiing improved each day. I had fun working my way up to harder and harder trails. Someday, I'll ski down the black diamond trails, like Mike.

There was a race at the end of my vacation. It's called "Cardboard Classic." Teams build "snowships" out of cardboard boxes. Mike and I made a snowship shaped like a giant shark. Mike thought that the snowship would go faster if it had a pointy tip like a shark's nose.

Mike was right! Our shark snowship zipped down the slope ahead of the others. Our pictures were in the newspaper the next day.

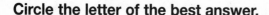

Circle the letter of the best answer.

1. What conclusion can you draw about Tucson?

   A There aren't many schools there.

   B Many people live there.

   C Snow rarely falls there.

   D People often go there to ski.

2. The narrator fell down often because —

   A he was not athletic

   B the snow was soft

   C the ski instructor didn't do a good job

   D he was learning to ski

3. Black diamond trails are —

   A easy trails for beginner skiers

   B difficult for experienced skiers

   C the only kind of trail in Colorado

   D closed during the "Cardboard Classic"

4. What conclusion can you draw about the "Cardboard Classic"?

   A The shark snowship fell apart.

   B The "Cardboard Classic" awarded great prizes.

   C The narrator's team won the "Cardboard Classic."

   D Building a snowship takes a long time.

A **conclusion** is an idea you figure out from details you read. It is something that the author wants you to understand, but does not tell you.

To draw a conclusion,

- Think about details you read in the passage.
- Then think about what you already know about the subject.
- Use what you have read and what you know to draw a conclusion about what the author wants you to understand.

Here's How

Read these sentences. Use the details you read, as well as what you already know, to draw a conclusion about Ruth Hart.

Ruth Hart lives next door to us. We don't see her very often, though. She works on a cruise ship. Most passengers do not need medical help. But if they do, she can provide it.

Think About It

1. I can read from the passage that Ruth Hart works on a cruise ship giving medical help to passengers.

2. I know that people who give medical help are either doctors or nurses.

3. I can draw the conclusion that Ruth Hart is either a doctor or a nurse.

Predict

When you **predict,** you think about what you have read and what might happen.

- Read the title and look at any pictures. Form an idea about what the passage will be about.
- After you read each paragraph, think about what you have read. Try to predict what will happen next.
- Think about whether your predictions were right. Make new predictions.

Read this passage. Use the Reading Guide for tips that can help you to predict and draw conclusions about what the author wants you to understand.

Reading Guide

Read the title and look at the picture. Form an idea of what the passage will be about.

Think about what you read. Look for details that help you draw conclusions about Miami.

Think about the passengers Dr. Hart treats and the ones she sends to shore. Think about why she might do this.

DR. HART SHIPS OUT

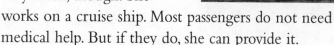

I live in Miami, Florida. People fly here from around the world. Many people board cruise ships. Most ships sail to the Caribbean. Someday, I'll sail to faraway lands, too. That's my dream!

Ruth Hart lives next door to us. We don't see her very often, though. She works on a cruise ship. Most passengers do not need medical help. But if they do, she can provide it.

Most cruise ship passengers have the same illness. They feel dizzy and get stomachaches. Others look pale. Choppy seas have gotten to them. They're seasick!

Dr. Hart treats them. Soon they feel better. Some cases are much more serious. People fall and break bones. Dr. Hart x-rays them on board. If the x-rays are hard to read, she scans them into her computer. Then she sends them to other doctors who are on shore.

If someone is really sick, she calls a helicopter. It flies the patient to a hospital at the nearest port.

Dr. Hart has fun at sea. I'd love to go as her helper!

Now use what you learned to draw conclusions.

Answer the questions on the next page.

Practice the Skill 1

Practice drawing conclusions in the passage you just read.

EXAMPLE

What conclusion can you draw about the hospitals on land?

A They are not good at treating seasickness.

B They can do some things Dr. Hart cannot do.

C Dr. Hart can do some things they cannot do.

D They are not good at treating broken bones.

Look for details as you read.

I read that Dr. Hart sometimes sends her patients to a hospital on land if they have serious problems.

Think about what you know.

I know that a doctor might send patients to another hospital if the other hospital can do more for them.

Combine what you read with what you know to form a reasonable conclusion.

I can conclude that hospitals on land are better at treating serious problems.

Now read each question. Circle the letter of the best answer.

1. What conclusion can you draw about Miami?

   A It is a very old and beautiful city.

   B It is near the ocean.

   C It has a very small airport.

   D Many cruise ships are built there.

2. Why doesn't the narrator see Dr. Hart very often?

   A Dr. Hart does not like the narrator.

   B Dr. Hart spends most of her time visiting friends.

   C Dr. Hart spends most of her time on a cruise ship.

   D Dr. Hart spends most of her time at a hospital.

3. Seasickness is probably —

   A an experience everyone has

   B quite rare among ship passengers

   C a very serious disease

   D a common illness on ships

4. How does Dr. Hart probably send x-rays to other doctors?

   A She uses the Internet on her computer.

   B She uses a fax machine.

   C She has a special radio that allows her to talk to other doctors.

   D A mail carrier often visits the ship to take the x-rays to shore.

NEWS FLASH!

Caves Crawling with New Species

This scorpion-like creature is one of 27 new species discovered.

THREE RIVERS, CA—Glowing orange spiders. Insects with see-through skin. Scorpions without tails. These are just three of the 27 new **species** of creepy crawlers scientists have found. They found them while exploring the caves beneath Sequoia National Park and Kings Canyon in California.

Scientists are excited to have found such unusual creatures. One bug is so clear you can see its insides. Another daddy longlegs has jaws bigger than its body. Scientists think these strange features have helped them live in the dark and damp caves.

Caves and the deep sea are some of the only places where scientists are still finding new species. Both places are difficult to explore. Scientists have just begun to study these animals. They are eager to find out how they live and why they look the way they do.

Write About It

Now you will practice the skill using a real news story. Complete this graphic organizer by filling in the first two boxes that lead to the given conclusion.

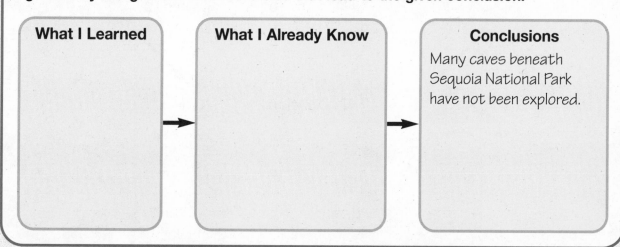

What I Learned

→

What I Already Know

→

Conclusions
Many caves beneath Sequoia National Park have not been explored.

A **conclusion** is a judgment you form based on details you read. It is something that the author wants you to understand but sometimes does not state directly.

Review the steps you can use to draw conclusions.

- Think about the details you read in the passage.
- Then think about what you already know about the subject.
- Use what you have read and what you know to draw a conclusion about the subject.

Practice 1

Read the following passage. As you read, think about what the author wants you to understand about what Sam Maverick did.

> Sam Maverick was a Texas cattleman and landowner. He lived in San Antonio during the mid-1800s. He owned a big herd of cows. He refused to use branding irons to burn marks on his animals. Maverick knew the burns would hurt the cattle. He became well known because he didn't follow the crowd. Today, the word *maverick* refers to someone who thinks differently from most people.

Draw a conclusion about why Sam Maverick did not brand his cattle. Use this diagram.

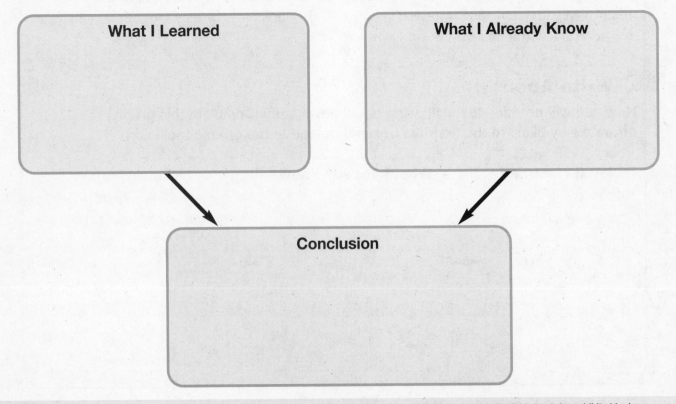

What I Learned

What I Already Know

Conclusion

Practice 2

Read this passage. What conclusion can you draw about why more kids are going to gyms?

A new gym has opened in Pennsylvania, and no adults are allowed. The new gym is just for kids. It has weights and other equipment that are designed for kids, and it is full of bright colors. Some equipment is connected to video games, so kids can have fun while they exercise.

This gym is part of a new **trend.** More and more kids are going to health clubs and gyms. Almost 5 million people under 18 use gyms outside of school. Parents are encouraging their children to go. Joining a gym can be expensive for parents. However, they say it's worth it to help their kids stay in shape.

Use the spaces on these diagrams to draw a conclusion about why more kids are going to gyms.

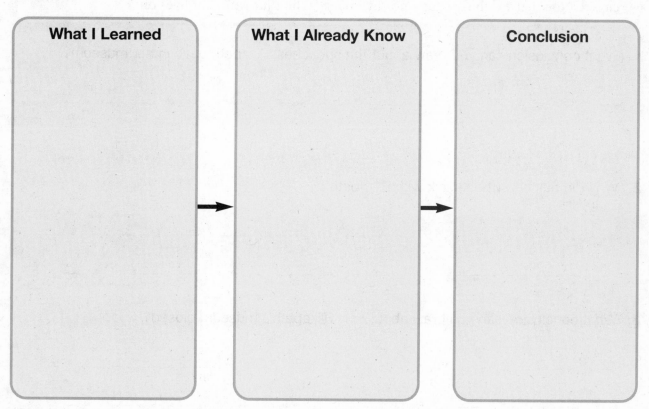

What I Learned	What I Already Know	Conclusion

Practice 3

Read this passage. Then draw conclusions to answer the questions. Make a graphic organizer on a separate sheet of paper to help you organize your thoughts.

Some people are "nuts" about their hobbies. Elizabeth Tashjian is one of these people. She loved nuts so much that she ran a Nut Museum in her house for about 30 years. The museum made her famous. She was often on TV. Talk show hosts loved to talk with her about her strange museum.

The price to enter Elizabeth's museum was three dollars and one nut. The Nut Museum had many exhibits. Some told facts about nuts. Some were artistic. There were paintings of nuts, sculptures of nuts, even masks made from nuts! There were hundreds of nutcrackers on display too. Elizabeth gave visitors tours of the museum, then gave a speech. After that, she usually sang a song that she made up. She called the song "Nuts Are Beautiful."

Elizabeth lived in her museum. When she grew older, she became ill and her museum closed. Now her exhibits are at a nearby college. The Nut Museum lives on!

1. What conclusion can you draw about the speeches Elizabeth gave in her museum?

_____

_____

2. Why did talk show hosts talk with Elizabeth?

_____

_____

3. What conclusion can you draw about why Elizabeth's museum closed?

_____

_____

Introduction

Sometimes a writer does not state things directly but instead gives you hints. You can combine these hints with what you already know to **draw a conclusion** about what the author is trying to say.

As you saw on pages 83–85, graphic organizers can help readers draw conclusions.

- In the first box, write details that you learned by reading.
- In the second box, write ideas you already know about the topic.
- Use the information in those two boxes to draw a conclusion. Write your conclusion in the third box.

Here's How

Read these sentences. What conclusion can you draw about Dusty?

Dusty doesn't look like a metal man. He looks like a metal dish on wheels. He has batteries inside that make him roll along the floor.

Think About It

What I Learned	What I Already Know	Conclusions
Dusty is made of metal and has batteries that make him roll along the floor.	Machines are often made of metal and have batteries.	Dusty is a machine.

Try This Strategy

Summarize

When you **summarize,** you think about the most important ideas that you read.

- When you finish reading a paragraph, think about the main ideas.
- Tell what the main ideas are in your own words.
- If you have trouble thinking of the main ideas, reread the section.

Read the story. Use the Reading Guide for tips that can help you to summarize and draw conclusions as you read.

Reading Guide

Think about how the narrator and Mom feel. Why does Mom shake her head?

Think of what you read about Ruby. Can you draw a conclusion about Ruby?

Summarize the main idea and details of the passage in your own words. How can they help you draw conclusions about what you read?

ROBOT TIDIES UP

I thought robots were supposed to be metal men. I imagined training one to do homework, make my bed, and bring me snacks. I sighed when Dad brought Dusty home. Mom just shook her head and said "Another crazy, expensive gadget that we don't need!"

Dusty doesn't look like a metal man. He looks like a metal dish on wheels. He has batteries inside that make him roll along the floor. While Dusty rolls, he cleans the floor!

Dusty spends a lot of time in the family room, picking up hair that Ruby has shed. If we set a timer, Dusty will clean while we're sleeping. He can tell if he is going over thick rugs or bare floors. He can even move under beds and around corners. Another sensor keeps him from falling downstairs.

When Dusty senses that a room is clean, he'll go back to his base, toot a horn, and recharge his batteries. Yesterday, I heard Mom tell her best friend, "That crazy gadget is pretty smart!"

This robot is supposed to clean so that families have more time together. There's just one problem. When Dusty starts cleaning, I like to watch him go, and Mom likes to take Ruby for a walk.

Answer the questions on the next page.

Practice the Skill 2

Practice drawing conclusions by answering questions about the story you just read. Read each question. Circle the letter of the best answer.

1. When Dad brings Dusty home, the narrator is —

   A excited

   B nervous

   C disappointed

   D happy

2. From the passage, you can conclude that Dad —

   A owns lots of robots

   B does not like to buy new things

   C is always trying to get out of cleaning

   D often brings home new gadgets

3. Because they have Dusty, the narrator's family might not need —

   A a wastebasket

   B a pet

   C a vacuum cleaner

   D a talking robot

4. What conclusion can you draw about Ruby?

   A Ruby is the narrator's sister.

   B Ruby is the narrator's dog.

   C Ruby is the narrator's pet bird.

   D Ruby has long black hair.

5. At the end of the story, the author wants you to understand that —

   A the narrator's mother has learned to live with Dusty

   B the narrator still wishes Dusty could do his homework

   C everyone should have a robot like Dusty

   D Dusty needs new batteries

6. On a separate sheet of paper, write a conclusion you could draw about what might happen if most families could afford to buy Dusty.

Trappers Catch 10-Foot Alligator

Professional trappers captured an alligator after wrestling with it for 15 minutes.

EAST HOUSTON, TX—A 10-foot alligator that had been trapped in a ditch in East Houston was finally caught. The Parks and Wildlife Department had tried to catch the gator, but the animal was too big for them to handle. Professional trappers were called in. They roped the alligator and pulled it to the top of the ditch, where it was captured without being hurt.

The alligator had been swimming in the ditch for several weeks. It drew crowds of local residents. Some people even threw pieces of chicken to the big gator. Many were worried that the animal might attack neighborhood pets or children. There were reports that some residents thought about trying to remove the alligator themselves. Most were happy to see the animal taken away.

The Parks and Wildlife Department warned people that feeding or coming near a wild animal is very dangerous. Feeding wild animals teaches them to think of food when they see humans. This can lead to even more **encounters** as animals come into cities and towns looking for a meal.

Write About It

Read this sentence from the article: "Most were happy to see the animal taken away." On a separate sheet of paper, explain how you think the writer drew this conclusion. Include what you already know about people's reactions to having dangerous animals in their neighborhoods as well as details from the article.

Read this article about fortune cookies. Then answer the questions on the next page.

The Fascinating Fortune Cookie

You've probably had one at the end of a meal of chop suey or egg foo yung. They might give you advice or tell you about the future. So where do these fortune cookies come from, anyway?

A legend says that the idea for fortune cookies comes from 14th-century China. At the time, China was controlled by the Mongols. A Chinese leader wanted to send a message to the people. He wanted to tell them when to fight the Mongols. However, he had to keep his messages a secret.

The man disguised himself as a priest. Then he put his messages in moon cakes, which he knew the Mongols would not eat. He passed the cakes to the Chinese people. When they read the messages inside, they knew when to begin fighting. They were able to take back their land thanks to the messages in the moon cakes.

Today's fortune cookies, however, are American inventions, not Chinese. The first real fortune cookie was probably made in San Francisco in 1914. The owner of a Japanese restaurant gave out cookies with thank-you notes inside them, and they were a hit.

Fortune cookies soon became popular in Chinese restaurants. Unlike the Chinese, Americans expected to have dessert after a meal. This was an easy way to offer dessert.

Today, most fortune cookies are made in one factory in Queens, New York. The Wonton Food Company makes almost 2.5 million cookies each day. The cookies start out as flat circles. Fortunes are dropped onto them before they are folded into their final shape. The fortunes are written by students, retired people, and writers.

Fortune cookies were not brought to China until 1993. That year, the Wonton Food Company opened a fortune cookie factory in China. However, the cookies never caught on. The idea fit better in America than in China.

Read each question. Circle the letter of the best answer.

1. Egg foo yung is most likely a kind of —

   A Chinese dessert
   B American breakfast
   C Chinese meal
   D fortune cookie

2. What can you conclude about the Mongols?

   A They invented fortune cookies.
   B They did not like moon cakes.
   C They were friends with the Chinese.
   D They often ate moon cakes.

3. The Chinese leader probably disguised himself as a priest because —

   A he was sneaking into a church
   B priests often make moon cakes
   C the Mongols would not expect a priest to plan a fight
   D the Mongols did not know who priests were

4. The Chinese were probably able to take back their land because —

   A they all fought at the same time
   B they were stronger than the Mongols
   C they disguised themselves as priests
   D they ate moon cakes

5. The first fortune cookies were probably served with —

   A Chinese food
   B Japanese food
   C American food
   D Mongolian food

6. Today, fortune cookies are —

   A not popular in China
   B becoming more popular in China
   C very popular in China
   D imported from China

7. When the fortune cookies are flat, they are probably —

   A hard
   B soft
   C fragile
   D unsweetened

8. On a separate sheet of paper, draw a conclusion about why the Wonton Food Company opened a fortune cookie factory in China in 1993.

Show What You Know

Before you begin this lesson, take this quiz to show what you know about interpreting figurative language. Read this story about a Halloween celebration. Then answer the questions.

HALLOWEEN HIJINKS

I love making slimy worms, dusty cobwebs, and spooky ghosts. That's why every Halloween I'm busy as a bee at the community center!

The other kids and I turn the center into a haunted house that's more fun than a barrel of monkeys. We stretch cotton balls into cobwebs and use wet noodles for worms. The paper ghosts always send a chill down my spine. We make sure all the lights are dim and use special green light bulbs. Sometimes we even use dry ice to make a mist that crawls along the floor like a snake. Of course, no haunted house is complete without spooky music. Then we all dress up in our scariest costumes and greet our guests!

Many kids and their parents stop by to feast their eyes on our display. People of all ages like to come and be scared by the haunted house we created. The whole community center comes alive with screams and laughter.

Circle the letter of the best answer.

1. Why might the writer compare herself to a bee in the first paragraph?

   A Bees are very hard working.

   B Bees are very scary.

   C She likes to wear yellow.

   D Halloween candy is sweet, like honey.

2. In the second paragraph, the phrase "a barrel of monkeys" means —

   A something that is scary

   B something that is noisy

   C something that is fun

   D something that is round

3. When the writer says kids and parents "feast their eyes," she means they —

   A eat a large and delicious meal

   B wear glasses to see more clearly

   C look at something delightful

   D look at something that makes them hungry

4. If the community center "comes alive," it probably —

   A begins to move

   B becomes noisy and lively

   C wakes up from a long sleep

   D glows in the dark

Introduction

Authors use **figurative language** to describe things in creative ways. Figurative language often makes a comparison that forms a picture in a reader's mind.

To interpret figurative language,

- Look for words that are used in surprising ways. A phrase might have a new meaning, or it might compare two things.
- Look for clues about what the words mean. The words *like* or *as* can be signs of a comparison.
- Use the clues to interpret figurative language. When things are compared, think about how they might be similar.

Here's How

Read these sentences. Look for an example of figurative language.

The museum was at a crayon factory. Going inside was like walking into a rainbow.

Think About It

1. The phrase *like walking into a rainbow* is surprising. They aren't really walking into a rainbow.

2. The crayon factory is being compared to a rainbow. A rainbow is very colorful.

3. The writer used these words to show that the crayon factory was very colorful.

Try This Strategy

Visualize

When you **visualize,** you picture in your mind the objects that the writer describes.

- Carefully read how the writer describes a person, a place, or a thing.
- Create a picture in your mind of what the writer describes.
- Look for things that are compared. Picture the two things in your mind. Imagine how they might be alike.

Read this passage. Use the Reading Guide for tips that can help you to visualize and interpret the figurative language.

Reading Guide

The writer compares Ms. Ames to a mouse. Think about qualities both share.

If you don't understand a word or phrase, see if you can use your own words to say the same thing.

Picture the descriptions the writer uses. Think about how these descriptions create a picture in your mind.

INTO THE RAINBOW

"Where are we going?" I asked. Ms. Ames was as quiet as a mouse. She wanted the class field trip to be a surprise. When the bus stopped, Ms. Ames spilled the beans. "Welcome to the crayon museum," she said. At first I thought the museum would be a yawn, but I was wrong. Our field trip was really fun!

The museum was at a crayon factory. Going inside was like walking into a rainbow. We saw their very first box of crayons. It had eight crayons, and only cost five cents. What a steal!

The tour guide asked a lot of questions. Which colors are cool? Which colors are as dull as dirt? The factory wanted to make new crayons that kids would like. They actually wanted to know what we thought! We felt like kings and queens.

The guide gave us each a free box of crayons. What a colorful day!

Now use what you learned to practice interpreting figurative language.

Answer the questions on the next page.

Practice the Skill 1

Practice interpreting figurative language in the passage you just read.

EXAMPLE

Why is Ms. Ames compared to a mouse in the passage?

A because she was quiet
B because she was noisy
C because she was small
D because she was sneaky

Look for words used in surprising ways.

The phrase *as quiet as a mouse* is a surprising description for Ms. Ames.

Decide what things are being compared.

Ms. Ames is compared to a mouse.

Think about what is similar about the things being compared.

Ms. Ames is being quiet, like a mouse. The writer wants us to know how quiet Ms. Ames is.

Now read each question. Circle the letter of the best answer.

1. When the writer says that Ms. Ames *spilled the beans,* it probably means that —

   A she dropped food on the floor
   B she helped someone spell a new word
   C she stopped the school bus
   D she told a secret

2. If a color is as *dull as dirt,* it is probably —

   A dark
   B boring
   C bright
   D exciting

3. Why was the box of crayons *a steal?*

   A It cost very little.
   B It cost too much.
   C It was free.
   D It was stolen.

4. Why does the narrator say that the kids felt like kings and queens?

   A They felt rich.
   B They felt excited.
   C They felt important.
   D They felt old-fashioned.

LAND OF 1,000 JOKES

The mayor of Normal wants to hear a new joke.

NORMAL, IL—It may be just a "normal" town, but it sure has an unusual name! The town of Normal, Illinois, has kept visitors laughing since it was formed in the 1800s. For some Normal residents, the jokes are growing tired. "Sometimes when people make the same joke you've heard a thousand times, it gets old," says Chris Koos, the mayor of Normal. "But you try to play along."

Koos says he'll give a $50 or $100 bill to anyone who comes up with a Normal joke he hasn't heard. So far he has been able to keep his money. Some of the most common jokes Koos and other residents have heard include, "What's next to Normal, abnormal?" and "Is everything really normal in Normal?"

Some town residents, known as Normalites, often tell people they are from nearby Bloomington to stop the **wisecracks.** Most businesses also avoid the jokes by not using the word Normal in their store name. Visitors looking for Normal Pizza or Normal Books are out of luck!

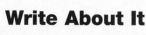

Write About It

In the first paragraph the author says that the jokes about Normal are "growing tired." Look for clues about what the phrase means. Write them in the second column. Write what the phrase means in the third column.

Figurative Language	Clues	Meaning
The jokes are growing tired.		

Ladder to Success

Review

You have learned that authors sometimes use **figurative language** to create an image in the reader's mind. **Figurative language** often compares two things to describe something.

Review the steps for interpreting figurative language.

- Look for a place where words are used in surprising ways.
- Search for clues about what the words mean. Sometimes the words *like* and *as* tell you there is a comparison. Look for what is being compared.
- Interpret the figurative language. Picture the two things being compared, and imagine how they are alike.

Practice 1

Read the following passage. As you read, look for examples of figurative language.

> One day Raja was feeling under the weather. He shook like a leaf! The doctor said that Raja had eaten too many cookies. Raja lives in a temple in Sri Lanka, and visitors give him tons of treats. But Raja is an elephant! Elephants like vegetables, not cookies. Now Raja's fit as a fiddle again, and the temple has a new sign. It says, "DO NOT feed the elephant!"

Now fill in this graphic organizer to interpret the figurative language. Use clues from the passage to find the meanings of the phrases *shook like a leaf* and *fit as a fiddle.*

Figurative Language	Clues	Meaning
shook like a leaf		
fit as a fiddle		

Practice 2

Read this passage. As you read, think about the meanings of the figurative language you find in the passage.

> Dad was reading a magazine when suddenly he turned to me. "Maria, look at this. A furry crab!" he said.
>
> "You're pulling my leg," I laughed.
>
> "I'm not joking. Look at it," Dad said. In the photograph, I could see the crab clearly. It was covered in fluffy white hair.
>
> "It's as black as night when it's deep in the ocean," Dad said. "There's no sunlight, so the crab doesn't need eyes. That fluffy hair might help it sense things nearby."
>
> "If I saw that in real life, I'd jump out of my skin!" I said.

Use this graphic organizer to interpret the figurative language that the writer uses. Use clues from the passage to find the meaning of the phrases.

Figurative Language	Clues	Meaning
pulling my leg		
black as night		
jump out of my skin		

Practice 3

Read this passage. Look for examples of figurative language. Then answer the questions. Make a graphic organizer on a separate sheet of paper to organize your thoughts.

Sara Renner was fighting like a tiger to keep moving across the snowy ground. She was cross-country skiing in the 2006 Winter Olympics, but one of her poles had just snapped. Three other skiers passed her, and her chances of winning a medal seemed to disappear.

Then, out of the blue, another pole appeared. She was very surprised. She grabbed it, and moved like the wind. Sara's sprint helped Canada win a silver medal. But who had given her the pole?

The mystery man turned out to be Bjornar Hakensmoen, a coach for Norway. Why would one of her opponents lend her a hand? "Winning is not everything in sports," Bjornar said. "What win is that, if you achieve your goal but don't help somebody when you should have helped them?"

Bjornar's Norwegian team came in fourth place, just short of an Olympic medal. But no one is upset that he helped Canada get ahead. "They expect me to do such things," he said. For Bjornar Hakensmoen, honor is head and shoulders above winning.

1. Why does the writer compare Sara Renner to a tiger?

_____

_____

2. What does the phrase *head and shoulders above* mean?

_____

_____

3. What does the writer mean by *out of the blue?* How do you know?

_____

_____

Guided Instruction 2

Writers use **figurative language** to describe things in a colorful way. Figurative language may compare one thing to another or use a phrase in a new way.

As you saw on pages 97–99, graphic organizers can help you interpret figurative language.

- Identify the figurative language and write it in the first box.
- In the second box, tell how the two objects being compared are alike.
- In the last box, write the meaning of the figurative language.

Here's How

Read the sentence. How do ants help describe the workers?

Everyone pitched in. We worked like an army of ants to clean up the trash and get rid of the weeds.

Think About It

Things Compared	How They Are Alike	Meaning
people working, an army of ants	Ants work together and work hard, and people can do this too.	They worked very hard and worked together.

Use Prior Knowledge

When you **use prior knowledge,** you think about what you already know.

- Think about what you already know about the topic.
- As you read, think of how what you know helps you understand the passage.
- If something is compared using figurative language, think of what you know about the things being compared.

Read the passage. Use the Reading Guide for tips that can help you use prior knowledge and interpret figurative language.

Reading Guide

What do you know about snapping your fingers? Does it take a lot of work or a little?

Mr. Cromwell compares the lot to a pancake. How does what you know about pancakes help describe the lot?

Look for comparisons in the passage. Why does the writer compare these objects?

BUILDING CROMWELL PARK

When you live downtown on a busy street, it can be hard to find a safe place to hang out. That's why I'm glad Mr. Cromwell moved to our neighborhood. "Count on me," he told our parents. "Getting a new playground will be a snap."

A week later, Mr. Cromwell called a meeting. "There's an empty lot on the corner of Wellington Street," he said. "It's as flat as a pancake, and it has some great trees. It would make a perfect playground. The city says we can take that lot off their hands. All we need to do is clean it up. Let's get everyone to lend a hand. Then, my company will donate a park design."

Everyone pitched in. We worked like an army of ants to clean up the trash and get rid of the weeds. When we were done, the lot sparkled like a diamond. Meanwhile, Mr. Cromwell drew a design for the park. My friend Daniel's father wrote to local businesses. He asked them to **contribute** funds to buy playground equipment.

Last week, our new playground opened. We named it Cromwell Park, in honor of the man who got the ball rolling for us.

Now use what you learned to interpret figurative language.

Answer the questions on the next page.

Practice interpreting figurative language. Read each question. Circle the letter of the best answer.

1. When Mr. Cromwell says building the new park will be "a snap," he means it —

   A will take a lot of work

   B will be noisy

   C will not be expensive

   D will be easy to do

2. Why does Mr. Cromwell compare a vacant lot to a pancake?

   A to show how warm it is

   B to show how round it is

   C to show how flat it is

   D to show how brown it is

3. When Mr. Cromwell says, "The city says we can take that lot off their hands," he probably means that the city —

   A will give them the lot

   B wants them to clean the lot

   C won't let them have the lot

   D wants them to return the lot after it's clean

4. Why does the writer compare the lot with a diamond?

   A to show how clean it is

   B to show how the lights made it shine

   C to show how bright it was in the sun

   D to show how valuable it was

5. When the writer says "the man who got the ball rolling," he probably means that Mr. Cromwell —

   A made a safe place to play ball

   B got plans started for the new park

   C got the lot cleaned up

   D got local businesses to donate sports equipment

6. In your own words, write what Mr. Cromwell means when he asks everyone to "lend a hand."

Strange Items Found In Drains

Animals, cannonballs, and toys have been found in sewers and drainpipes.

CINCINNATI, OH—These days, unclogging a drain can be like digging for buried treasure. Plumbers from the Roto-Rooter® company have been finding some strange things in people's pipes, toilets, and sewers. Some of the strange finds include toys, a cannonball, and a live cat. The list of items came from a survey taken by about 5,000 Roto-Rooter employees.

The unusual objects made their way down the drain in different ways. In Bloomington, Illinois, a 3-year-old boy was trying to train his G.I. Joe toys for water rescue. When the action figures did not return, he sent Matchbox cars to try to rescue them. Roto-Rooter employee Michael Woggon recovered 15 toys from the drainpipes.

In North Carolina, a live cat was found in a storm sewer. The Roto-Rooter crew had to dig through dirt and concrete to rescue the cat. Animals are one of the more common things discovered in sewers and drainpipes. With animals such as rattlesnakes, pigs, and skunks being found, the sewers and drainpipes are turning into jungles!

Write About It

Read this sentence from the article: "These days, unclogging a drain can be like digging for buried treasure." It uses figurative language. On a separate sheet of paper, explain why the writer chose to compare unclogging a drain to digging for buried treasure.

Read this article about an artist. Then answer the questions on the next page.

The Strange Art of Jackson Pollock

Imagine a painting that's as busy as a city street. The painting isn't of a person or a place. Instead it's like a puzzle that you have to figure out. There are colorful lines, **splotches,** and drips, but no objects. This is the strange style of painting that Jackson Pollock introduced to the world. Today, Pollock's paintings hang in museums all over the world.

When Pollock was young, he made "regular" paintings. Like other artists, he used a paintbrush and an easel to create pictures of objects and people. But these paintings left him down in the dumps. He wasn't happy until he created a whole new style of painting. The two styles were like night and day.

First, he took his canvas off the easel and put it on the floor. Then he threw away his paintbrush. He dripped paint onto the canvas. He made splotches that looked like puddles and painted with a stick. He stuck sand, broken glass, and other things into the wet paint. He didn't try to control his work. He just let the paint drip and splatter on its own. "The painting has a life of its own," he said. "I try to let it come through."

In his lifetime, many people thought Pollock's art showed no skill. "It looks like the work of a chimpanzee!" some critics said. Pollock never hit it big, and he was always short on cash. However, years after his death, people changed their minds. Other artists said that he was great. Willem de Kooning, another modern artist, said that Pollock "broke the ice," leading the way into modern art by having new ideas and techniques.

Dive into the art of Jackson Pollock. Find his work in books or on the Internet. Look at the strange new methods that he used. What messages and mysteries do you see in those lines, splotches, and drips?

Read each question. Circle the letter of the best answer.

1. In the first paragraph, why does the writer compare the paintings of Jackson Pollock with a city street?

   A to show how strange they are

   B to show how new they are

   C to show how lively they are

   D to show how boring they are

2. What does the writer mean when she says that a Pollock canvas is "like a puzzle"?

   A The objects in the paintings are in pieces.

   B He hid words and funny sayings in his paintings.

   C The people in the paintings have puzzling appearances.

   D The paintings are hard to understand.

3. When the author says that the two styles Pollock used "were like night and day," she means —

   A the new style was much brighter

   B the new style was done during the day

   C the new style was very different

   D the new style was more popular

4. When Pollock says that a painting has "a life of its own," he means —

   A he paints pictures of animals

   B he doesn't plan what the painting will look like

   C he doesn't like to paint pictures of real things

   D the painting can move by itself

5. When Pollock was "down in the dumps," he was —

   A angry

   B curious

   C unhappy

   D excited

6. When the writer says Pollock "never hit it big," it probably means that Pollock —

   A never made large paintings

   B never got into fights

   C never made big splotches on his paintings

   D never gained a lot of money and success

7. What did de Kooning mean when he said that Pollock "broke the ice"?

   A Pollock led artists to try new ways to paint.

   B Pollock took unnecessary risks.

   C Pollock put broken glass on some of his paintings.

   D Pollock broke the law.

8. The writer encourages you to "dive into" the art of Jackson Pollock. What does the writer mean? Why might the writer use the image of a person diving?

LADDERS to SUCCESS

LESSON

8

Distinguishing
Between Real and
Make-Believe

Show What You Know

Before you begin this lesson, take this quiz to show what you know about real and make-believe. Read this story about a new neighbor. Then answer the questions.

My Mysterious New Neighbor

I heard a giggle from the doorway. Standing there was a tiny lady with white hair and a big, bright smile. It was our new neighbor, Mrs. Miller. She lifted her hand and waved. I wiggled my fingers back at her.

Without a word, she reached into her purse. Way in. In fact, her arm disappeared. But the bag wasn't that big! She seemed to be looking for something. Finally, she winked at me and pulled her arm back out of the bag. She was holding a chessboard. I wondered how that big chessboard had fit inside her little purse.

I jumped up and cleared off the table. She put down the chessboard and reached back into her magic purse. One by one, she took out the chess pieces. At first, they looked normal to me. When I looked again, though, they weren't normal at all. They were alive! All of them, the knight's horse, the king, the queen — alive! I had always loved chess, but this was something else! Mrs. Miller snapped her fingers. The chess pieces popped into their spots on the board.

Circle the letter of the best answer.

1. Which event could not happen in real life?

   A The narrator heard a giggle.

   B A tiny lady was standing in the doorway.

   C She lifted her hand and waved.

   D Her arm disappeared.

2. What tells you that this story might not be true?

   A She reached into her purse.

   B She lifted her hand and waved.

   C She snapped her fingers.

   D She pulled a big chessboard out of her little purse.

3. Which of these could be real?

   A a magical new neighbor

   B chess pieces popping into their spots on the board

   C a boy who loves chess

   D a big chessboard coming out of a small purse

4. Which of these is make-believe?

   A a small purse

   B chess pieces that are alive

   C a tiny lady with frizzy, white hair

   D a big chessboard

Real people, places, and things actually exist or could exist. Events that actually happen or could happen are real. **Make-believe** people, places, and things could not exist. Events that couldn't happen are make-believe.

To distinguish between real and make-believe,

- Think about what you are reading. Ask yourself: *Could this actually exist? Could this happen in real life?*

- If what you are reading about could happen in real life, then it is real. If it could not happen, then it is make-believe.

Here's How

Read these sentences. Which parts could be real? Which parts are make-believe?

"I heard you crying from 100 miles away with my super-hearing."
Zach looked like a regular boy. His purple suit had an orange "Z" on it.

Think About It

1. *I see that Zach heard someone crying from 100 miles away. I know that real people cannot hear from that far. Zach's "super-hearing" is make-believe.*

2. *I read that Zach looked like a regular boy. The purple suit could exist. Those parts could be real.*

Visualize

When you **visualize,** you make a picture of what you are reading in your mind.

- Think about what you read. Pay attention to the details.

- Carefully read how the writer describes the characters, setting, and events.

- Use the details and descriptions to make pictures in your mind. When you picture events, think of them as a movie happening in your mind.

Read the story. Use the Reading Guide for tips that can help you visualize and distinguish between real and make-believe as you read.

Reading Guide

Think about the things Kim says and does. Would a real person act this way?

Visualize Zach lifting the boulder. Pay attention to the details. Could a boy actually do this?

Visualize Zach calling to Polly. Pay attention to the details the writer uses to describe this event. Real people do not have super powers.

Zach Dynamo, young superhero

"My parakeet!" Kim sobbed. "She's gone forever!" Kim had forgotten to close Polly's cage, and the parakeet had flown away.

"It's okay," she heard someone say. "I'll find your bird."

Kim turned. "Zach Dynamo!" Kim screamed. "Here? In my backyard?"

"Of course," Zach replied. "I heard you crying from 100 miles away with my super-hearing."

Zach looked like a regular boy. His purple suit had an orange "Z" on it.

"You're smaller than I thought you'd be," she said.

"I may not be tall, but I'm strong. See?" Zach picked up a boulder the size of a car. Kim was amazed by his super-strength.

"Can you — *hic!* — find Polly?" Kim asked. She had the hiccups from crying.

"Absolutely! I'll use my super bird-calling powers!" Zach whistled and chirped, exactly like Polly. A little yellow bird swooped down and perched on Zach's shoulder.

"Polly!" cried Kim. "Thank you, Zach Dynamo!"

"No problem," Zach said. "After all, I'm a superhero!"

"So, can you — *hic!* — help me with — *hic!* — these super-hiccups?" Kim asked.

"Gee, that's one power I just don't have," Zach told her.

Now use what you learned to distinguish between real and make-believe.

Answer the questions on the next page.

Practice the Skill 1

Practice distinguishing between real and make-believe in the story you just read.

EXAMPLE

Which of the following could not be real?

A The parakeet flew away.

B Kim forgot to close Polly's cage.

C Zach whistled and chirped, exactly like Polly.

D A little yellow bird swooped down and perched on Zach's shoulder.

Look for details about characters, settings, or events.

I read that Polly flew away because Kim left her cage open. I also read that Zach has super bird-calling power. When he whistles and chirps, it sounds just like any bird he wants.

Think about what could happen in real life. Think about what could never happen.

A boy can't have these super bird-calling powers. The other details could all happen in real life.

Tell what is not real.

A boy could not whistle and chirp exactly like a particular parakeet. This detail is make-believe.

Now read each question. Circle the letter of the best answer.

1. Which of these is make-believe?

   A A boy picks up a giant boulder.

   B A boy whistles.

   C A girl has the hiccups.

   D A girl sobs.

2. Which could never exist?

   A a superhero

   B a parakeet

   C a boulder

   D a backyard

3. Which of these could not happen?

   A A girl gets the hiccups from crying.

   B A parakeet flies away.

   C A boy has superpowers.

   D A boulder is as big as a car.

4. Which of these could be real?

   A Zach's hearing

   B Zach's strength

   C Zach's bird-calling powers

   D Kim's hiccups

MALAYSIA TEAM TO TRACK "BIGFOOT"

This photo, supposedly of Bigfoot, was taken in California in 1977.

KUALA LUMPUR, MALAYSIA—A team of scientists is looking for a beast known as "Bigfoot." The decision to search for Bigfoot was made after a sighting in Malaysia, an Asian country.

"The mystery of Bigfoot's existence has attracted a lot of interest," said one Malaysian official. He hoped the search would prove that the animal is real. The name Bigfoot is given to strange hairy beasts that walk on two legs. People around the world say they have seen Bigfoot. However, its existence has not been proven.

The latest Bigfoot sighting in Malaysia was in November 2005. Several farm workers reported that they saw three strange animals near a park. The farmers also said they saw a footprint that Bigfoot left behind.

Park officials searched the area. They did not find any clues that Bigfoot had been there. Several other Bigfoot sightings were reported later. Villagers living near the park said they saw the hairy beast.

Write About It

Now you will practice the skill using a real news story. Complete this graphic organizer by giving reasons why Bigfoot may be real or make-believe. Include things you already know as well as details from the article.

Why Bigfoot Is Real	Why Bigfoot Is Make-Believe

LADDERS
to SUCCESS

LESSON
8
Distinguishing
Between Real and
Make-Believe

Ladder to Success

Review

As you read, you can **distinguish between real and make-believe.** Things that could actually exist or happen are real. Things that could not exist or happen are make-believe.

Review the steps you can use to distinguish between real and make-believe.

- Think about whether what you are reading could actually exist. Think about whether it could actually happen.
- If the person, place, thing, or event could exist or happen in real life, then it is real. If not, it is make-believe.

Practice 1

Read the following passage. As you read, think about the characters, setting, and events. Decide whether they are real or make-believe.

> When Paul Bunyan was a baby, he loved porridge. He ate forty bowls for breakfast. Soon, Paul was so big that he used wagon wheels for buttons on his clothes. Paul became a lumberjack. He could knock down twenty trees with one swing of his ax.
>
> One winter, Paul found a baby ox in the snow. Paul named the blue ox Babe. Babe ate one ton of grain each day.

Use the chart below to identify the parts of the passage that could happen and the parts that could not happen. Write an X in the correct column to tell if each detail could be real or is make-believe.

Detail From Passage	Could Be Real	Make-Believe
When Paul Bunyan was a baby, he loved porridge.		
When Paul Bunyan was a baby, he ate forty bowls of porridge for breakfast.		
Paul was so big that he used wagon wheels for buttons on his clothes.		
Paul became a lumberjack.		
He could knock down twenty trees with one swing of his ax.		
One winter, Paul found a baby ox in the snow.		
Paul named the blue ox Babe.		
Babe ate one ton of grain each day.		

Practice 2

Read the passage. Which ideas are real? Which ideas are make-believe?

Zylorg looked around at this strange place. Everywhere he looked, people walked around on two feet. It was very strange for him. He was used to the way things were on his planet, Kweevle. There, people walked on five legs. Also, all Kweevle animals could talk.

Zylorg wished he could hop in his spaceship and get away from this weird place. He wanted to turn his engines to hyper-warp speed and zip 50 billion miles away from Earth. These two-legged people made him nervous. And the Earth dogs confused him. Every time he asked one for directions, the silly thing just barked at him!

Use this graphic organizer to distinguish between real and make-believe details in the story.

Details That Could Be Real	Details That Are Make-Believe

Practice 3

Read the passage. Then distinguish between real and make-believe to answer the questions. Make a graphic organizer on a separate sheet of paper to organize your thoughts.

> Janet wanted to visit April 7, 1776. But she made a mistake entering the date into the control panel of her time machine. Instead of 4/7/1776, she typed 7/4/1776. It was the first Fourth of July!
>
> In school, Janet had read that July 4, 1776, was the day America gained independence. On her trip to 1776, Janet found out that was not the whole story.
>
> The Declaration of Independence was adopted on July 4, 1776. This means that patriots like Thomas Jefferson, Benjamin Franklin, and Samuel Adams all agreed to the Declaration on that day. Two days later, the Declaration was printed in the Philadelphia newspaper.
>
> On July 8, there was a big celebration in Independence Square. The Declaration was read out loud to the public. Bands played music. Church bells rang.
>
> What was the biggest surprise for Janet? The Declaration of Independence had not yet been signed on that first July Fourth! She learned later that it took months for the official copy to be signed by everyone.

1. Write two events in the story that happen in real life.

   _____

   _____

2. Tell one thing in the story that could not exist in real life.

   _____

   _____

3. Is this story real or make-believe? How do you know?

   _____

   _____

Introduction

Real things could actually exist or happen. **Make-believe** things could not exist or happen. You can decide whether the people, places, things, and events that you read about are real or make-believe. A story or passage can have some parts that are real and some parts that are make-believe.

As you saw on pages 111–113, graphic organizers help you distinguish between real and make-believe.

- Think about each person, place, thing, or event. Decide if it could exist or happen in real life.
- Find events that could really happen. Write an *X* in the "Real" section of the graphic organizer.
- Find events that could not happen. Write an *X* in the "Make-Believe" section.

Here's How

Read this paragraph. Which details could be real? Which are make-believe?

As he waited for the rain shower to pass, Hal looked back at the river where he had been swimming for hours. He remembered being in that water, with fins and a tail. He could still feel what it was like to breathe through gills.

Think About It

Detail From Passage	Real	Make-Believe
He waited for the rain shower to pass	X	
He remembered being in that water, with fins and a tail		X

Use Prior Knowledge

When you **use prior knowledge,** you use what you know to understand what you read.

- Read what the writer says about the story characters, setting, and events. Compare them to people, places, and events in your life.
- Use what you read and what you know to better understand the story.

Read the story. Use the Reading Guide for tips that can help you use prior knowledge and distinguish between real and make-believe as you read.

Reading Guide

Think about these events. Could they ever happen?

Can a person turn into a fish in real life?

Review the details the writer uses. Could the setting that is described be real? Could this place exist?

What do you know about people and fish? Could these memories be real?

HAL'S WISH

Oh, how I wish I could be a fish, Hal thought as he stared at the fish swimming in the river. Suddenly, Hal felt something strange. He felt like he was shrinking. Hal looked down. His legs were turning into a tail! He tried to reach for them, but his arms had become fins!

Before he knew it, Hal was in the water. He was a fish! *This is great!* Hal thought. Hal joined the school of fish as it moved through the water. He couldn't have been happier.

Hal swam for hours. Then it grew dark. The water felt cooler. There was a flash of light, and Hal was sitting at the edge of the river just as he had been before. Something wet plopped on his head, and a cool breeze whispered by. Hal looked up. A cloud covered the sun, and it had begun to rain. He ran to the tent.

As he waited for the rain shower to pass, Hal looked back at the river where he had been swimming. He remembered being in that water, with fins and a tail. He could still feel what it was like to breathe through gills. *Was that real, or did I imagine it?*

Now use what you learned to distinguish between real and make-believe.

Answer the questions on the next page.

Practice the Skill 2

Practice distinguishing between real and make-believe. Answer questions about the story you just read. Read each question. Circle the letter of the best answer.

1. Which of the following could not be real?

   A A boy wishes he could be a fish.

   B A boy turns into a fish.

   C A boy stares at fish.

   D A boy swims in a river for hours.

2. Which of the following is make-believe?

   A A cloud covered the sun.

   B It grew dark.

   C His arms had become fins.

   D It had begun to rain.

3. Which of the following could never happen?

   A Hal was sitting at the edge of the river.

   B Hal huddled in a tent with his family.

   C Hal looked back at the river.

   D Hal breathed through gills.

4. Which of these events could happen in real life?

   A A boy waits for a rain shower to pass.

   B A boy is shrinking.

   C A boy's legs are turning into a tail.

   D A boy pops out of the water in a flash of light.

5. Which of these could not happen in real life?

   A A cool breeze whispered by.

   B The water felt cooler.

   C Hal felt a strange sensation.

   D His legs were turning into a tail.

6. On a separate sheet of paper, tell whether this story is real or make-believe. Explain how you know.

ALAPAHA, GA—It's more than just a myth! The body of a huge **swine** known as "Hogzilla" was found in South Georgia. A team of experts with National Geographic led the project. They proved that the monster pig was real.

The team found that the "super swine" was not as super as some thought. People thought Hogzilla was 12 feet long and weighed 1,000 pounds. In fact, Hogzilla was probably 8 feet long and weighed 800 pounds. Most hogs only grow to about 150 pounds.

Still, the National Geographic team was **impressed.** "He was definitely a freak of nature," said producer Nancy Donnelly. Donnelly and her film crew filmed the project for a National Geographic show.

Hogzilla has caused quite a stir in the town of Alapaha. The town made Hogzilla the theme of its fall festival. Their parade featured a fake Hogzilla, and children wore pink pig outfits. There was even a Hogzilla princess!

Hogzilla was much bigger than this average hog.

"HOGZILLA"

Write About It

Find two facts about Hogzilla that were real. Then think of two things that could not be real about Hogzilla. Write them on a separate sheet of paper.

LADDERS to SUCCESS

LESSON

8

Distinguishing
Between Real and
Make-Believe

Show What You Learned

Read this passage about Johnny Appleseed. Then answer the questions on the next page.

Johnny Appleseed

Some people think Johnny Appleseed was not a real person, but he was. His real name was John Chapman. He was born in Massachusetts in 1775. His father fought in the first battle of the Revolutionary War. Johnny Chapman planted apple tree farms in the Midwest. Then he sold the young apple trees to settlers to plant on their own land. He wanted them to have enough to eat and he knew that apples were a healthy food. He believed that the trees would give settlers the food they needed.

Many make-believe stories have been written about Johnny. Some say that he wandered the country, scattering apple seeds everywhere. Some say that he never wore a pair of shoes in his life, even as he walked his way around the country, planting trees. One legend says that the soles of his feet were thick as leather. Others say that he wore a tin pot on his head like a hat.

Johnny Chapman was a gentle man who cared about animals. This has led to some other tall tales. In one story, Johnny discovered a bear and her cubs living in a hollow log. He had built his campfire against the log. According to the tale, Johnny put his fire out and slept that night in the snow. He didn't want to disturb the bears! In some versions of that tale, Johnny decided to climb into the log and sleep next to the bears. Still other stories tell that he made friends with the bears and played with them. Sleeping in the snow would have been nothing for Johnny, though. Many tall tales about Johnny tell how he made his drinking water by melting snow with his feet!

Johnny "Appleseed" Chapman spent almost 50 years of his life planting apple trees. He brought apple trees to Indiana, Illinois, Kentucky, Ohio, and Pennsylvania. Today, 200 years later, some of those trees are still producing apples.

Read each question. Circle the letter of the best answer.

1. Which event did not happen?

   A Johnny sold young apple trees to settlers.

   B Johnny planted apple tree farms in the Midwest.

   C Johnny cut down every apple tree in five states.

   D Johnny thought if the settlers had apple trees, they'd have plenty of food.

2. Which tells about something real?

   A He made drinking water by melting snow with his feet.

   B He spent almost 50 years planting apple trees.

   C He never wore a pair of shoes.

   D He wore a tin pot on his head.

3. Which of these is not real?

   A Johnny Appleseed is the subject of many tall tales.

   B Johnny's father fought in the Revolutionary War.

   C Johnny was born in Massachusetts in 1775.

   D The soles of Johnny's feet were thick as leather.

4. Which event could have happened?

   A Johnny discovered a bear and her cubs living in a hollow log.

   B Johnny decided to climb into the log and sleep next to the bears.

   C Johnny made friends with the bears and played with them.

   D Johnny talked to the bears and they talked back.

5. Which of these is make-believe?

   A Johnny Appleseed's real name was John Chapman.

   B Johnny knew that apples were a healthy food.

   C Johnny's trees still produce apples, 200 years later.

   D Johnny wandered the country, scattering apple seeds everywhere.

6. Which could not have happened?

   A Johnny cared about animals.

   B Johnny Appleseed planted magic apple trees.

   C Johnny wanted the pioneer settlers to have enough to eat.

   D Johnny built a campfire against the log.

7. Which of these was true in real life?

   A Johnny was gentle.

   B Johnny fought a bear.

   C Johnny cut down trees.

   D Johnny loved shoes.

8. On a separate sheet of paper, tell whether Johnny Appleseed was a real person. How do you know? Use information from the passage.

Show What You Know

Before you begin this lesson on determining author's purpose, take this quiz to show what you know. Read this story about an uncle's joke. Then answer the questions.

UNCLE BOB'S PRACTICAL JOKE
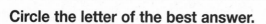

Uncle Bob loves to play jokes on people. Last week he played a joke on *me*.

The whole family went to Grandma's house for dinner. We were all supposed to bring something to eat, so I made chicken salad. When Mom and I got to Grandma's, Uncle Bob was just getting out of his car. "What did you bring, Jen?" he asked.

"Chicken salad," I said. I showed him the bowl I was carrying. Uncle Bob looked surprised.

"But I brought chicken salad, too!" he said.

"Oh no!" I said. "What do we do now?"

"Well, why don't you come look at the chicken salad I brought?" Uncle Bob said. He took a big box from his car. I heard clucking sounds. Inside was a live chicken covered in lettuce!

"Tricked you!" Uncle Bob said.

Mom laughed. "So that's why you asked me what Jen was bringing!" she said. I started laughing, too. Uncle Bob really got me!

Circle the letter of the best answer.

1. Which words best describe the passage?

    A sad and gloomy

    B stern and serious

    C light and funny

    D angry and intense

2. This story has all of the following except —

    A interesting characters

    B lively dialogue

    C an enjoyable plot

    D technical details

3. Which detail best supports the purpose of this article?

    A Jen made chicken salad.

    B Jen and her Mom laughed at the joke.

    C Uncle Bob looked surprised that Jen made chicken salad.

    D The whole family went to Grandma's for dinner.

4. The article mainly —

    A tells a funny story

    B persuades the reader to do something

    C explains how to do something

    D describes a family

Introduction

An **author's purpose** is the main reason why an author writes a story or article. An author may write to entertain you with a funny story. An author may also write to persuade you of something. Or the author may write to inform you about a topic, providing facts and details.

To determine the author's main purpose,

- Find what the passage is mostly about.

- Look at the words the author chooses. Are they funny and entertaining? Are they trying to convince me of something? Does the author use lots of facts?

- Use these clues to decide whether the author's purpose is to entertain, persuade, or inform.

Here's How

Read these sentences. What is the author's main purpose?

Cockroaches often live in damp places such as basements and kitchen sinks. Most people do not want cockroaches in their buildings. Not Michael Bohdan. He started a cockroach museum in Texas. His museum is called the Cockroach Hall of Fame.

Think About It

1. This passage is about a cockroach museum.

2. The passage does not use funny words or convincing language. The author gives many details about the topic.

3. The author's purpose is to inform.

Predict

When you **predict,** you think about what the passage will be about.

- Read the title and look at any pictures. Predict what the passage will be about. As you read, predict what you will find out next.

- Check your predictions at the end to see if you were correct.

Read this passage. Use the Reading Guide for tips. The tips will help you preview and predict and determine the author's purpose as you read.

Reading Guide

What do the title and the picture suggest about the author's main purpose for writing?

In the first paragraph, the author states that Michael Bohdan started a cockroach museum. Make a prediction about what the museum will be like.

Think about what kind of details the author provides. Decide if they are entertaining, persuasive, or factual.

THE COCKROACH MUSEUM

A cockroach is a small, reddish-brown bug. Cockroaches often live in damp places such as basements and kitchen sinks. Most people do not want cockroaches in their buildings. Not Michael Bohdan. He started a cockroach museum in Texas. His museum is called the Cockroach Hall of Fame.

Michael's museum contains cockroaches dressed in **outlandish** costumes. Michael collects his "Roach Art" by holding a costume contest every year. People send in roaches dressed in strange suits. One roach was dressed as Batman. Of course, it was named Batroach! One person sent a group of roaches in a tiny diner. Some sat at tables. Others wore aprons and cooked in the kitchen.

Michael has been a pest specialist for more than 20 years. He helps remove cockroaches and other pests from people's homes. Now instead of just removing cockroaches, he also collects them.

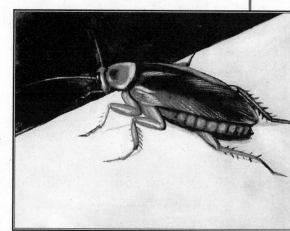

Now use what you learned to determine the author's purpose.

Answer the questions on the next page.

Determine the author's purpose of the story you just read.

EXAMPLE

Most of the author's details about the museum are —

A sad
B informative
C persuasive
D cheerful

Think of what the passage is about.

The passage is about a cockroach museum.

Look for specific words the author chooses. Are they silly, informative, persuasive, or cheerful?

Most of the details in the passage are facts. They inform about the cockroach museum. They are not sad or cheerful. They are not trying to persuade the reader.

Now read each question. Circle the letter of the best answer.

1. Which is the best alternate title for this article?

   A The Cockroach Hall of Fame
   B How to Kill Cockroaches
   C What Roaches Like to Wear
   D Something to Make You Sick

2. Which detail does not inform about the cockroach museum?

   A Michael Bohdan started the museum.
   B The museum is called the Cockroach Hall of Fame.
   C Most people don't like cockroaches in their buildings.
   D The museum contains roaches dressed in outlandish costumes.

3. Why does the author state that the museum is in Texas?

   A to persuade the reader to move to Texas
   B to make the reader laugh
   C to explain how to get to the museum
   D to provide a detail about the museum

4. What is the author's purpose in writing this article?

   A to tell an exciting story
   B to describe something
   C to convince the reader about something
   D to explain how to do something

9-Year-Old Swims from Alcatraz to San Francisco

Nine-year-old Johnny Wilson making the tough swim from Alcatraz to San Francisco.

SAN FRANCISCO, CA—Go, Johnny, Go! Nine-year-old Johnny Wilson from Hillsborough swam all the way from Alcatraz to San Francisco. Wilson became the youngest athlete ever to complete the 1.4-mile swim.

The swim from Alcatraz Island to San Francisco is a **challenging** one. The choppy waters and rough winds will slow down swimmers of any age. There are also sharks found in that part of the San Francisco Bay. But nothing could slow the adventurous fourth-grader down. Wilson dove right into the cold, 53-degree water at the crack of dawn. He swam almost non-stop to Aquatic Park in San Francisco.

Chants of "Go, Johnny! Go, Johnny!" greeted Wilson as he neared the shore. He was mobbed by friends, family, and reporters before he could even step on dry land! After Wilson answered a few questions, Wilson's father brought him home for some much-needed rest.

Write About It

Now you will practice the skill using a real news article. Complete this graphic organizer by filling in the author's purpose in writing this article. Use sentences from the article to help you find your answer.

Author's Purpose

Sentence
Go, Johnny, Go!

Sentence
But nothing could slow the adventurous fourth-grader down.

Sentence
He was mobbed by friends, family, and reporters before he could even step on dry land!

Review

You are learning how to **determine the author's purpose.** The **author's purpose** is the main reason the author wrote a passage. Authors write to inform, to persuade, or to entertain.

Review the steps that will help you determine the author's purpose.

- Ask yourself, "What is the passage mainly about?"
- Look for words and phrases that are entertaining or persuasive.
- Look for facts and details that inform you about something.
- Decide if the author has written to entertain you, to persuade you, or to give you information about a topic.

Practice 1

Read the following passage. As you read, think about the author's main purpose for writing. Is the author's purpose to inform, persuade, or entertain?

> People get careless when they are in a hurry. They may even cross the street when they're not supposed to. This is a bad idea. Cars can be very dangerous.
>
> Make sure you look both ways before crossing the street. Cross only when the cars have stopped moving or when there are no cars coming. Then you will be a lot safer.

Fill in the boxes below. First, write the topic of the passage. Then write words or phrases that provide clues to the author's purpose. In the last box, describe the author's purpose.

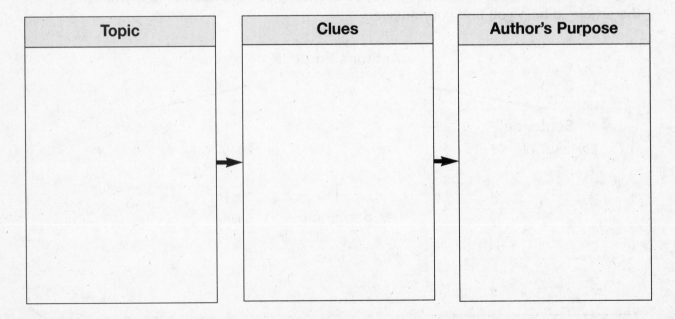

Topic	Clues	Author's Purpose

Practice 2

Read this passage. Determine the author's main purpose for writing.

> The zinnia is a lovely flower. It has lots of pointed petals. The petals may be red, orange, yellow, or white. They shoot out from a bright yellow center.
>
> Many gardeners plant zinnia seeds. The seeds sprout quickly. Then the plants grow tall and thick. Zinnias don't mind the long, hot days of summer. They don't need a lot of water to survive.
>
> The zinnia is named after a scientist who lived long ago. His name was Johann Zinn. Zinn spent his life studying plants.

Use this graphic organizer to determine the author's purpose.

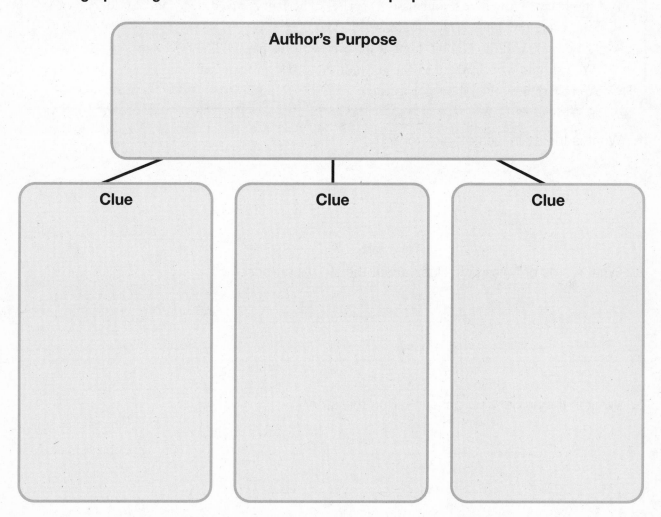

Author's Purpose

Clue

Clue

Clue

Practice 3

Read this passage. Then answer the questions to determine the author's purpose. Make a graphic organizer on a separate sheet of paper to organize your thoughts.

Once upon a time a Rabbit lived in a forest. The Rabbit had small ears, just like the other animals in the forest. The Rabbit loved to spy on the other animals.

One day a Fairy caught the Rabbit listening to two animals having a conversation. "Oh Rabbit!" said the Fairy. "You shouldn't spy on the other animals." The Rabbit laughed at the Fairy. "I can do what I want!" he said.

The Fairy frowned. "If you spy on the other animals one more time, I will give you a nasty surprise," she said. The Rabbit just kept laughing.

A few days later the Fairy caught the Rabbit spying on two more animals. "That's it!" said the Fairy. "Now here's your nasty surprise!" The Fairy waved her wand. Suddenly the Rabbit's ears grew longer and longer.

"My ears!" said the Rabbit. He felt his ears with his paws. "They're huge!"

"You should have listened to me and not the other animals," said the Fairy.

And that's how the rabbit got its ears.

1. What is the main idea of this story?

_____

_____

2. What words or ideas give clues about the story's purpose?

_____

_____

3. What is the author's purpose in telling this story?

_____

_____

An author writes a passage to entertain, persuade, or inform. Two ways an author can inform is to explain or describe something. You can use the main idea of the passage to help you **determine the author's purpose.**

As you saw on pages 125–127, graphic organizers can help readers determine the author's purpose.

- In the first box, write what the passage is mainly about.
- In the second box, write clues that help you determine the author's purpose.
- In the third box, write the author's purpose.

Here's How

Read these sentences. What clues can help you determine the author's purpose?

Bird feeders are a great way to give birds the extra food they need. You can make a bird feeder using a pinecone and a few other materials. Here is how to make your own pinecone bird feeder.

Think About It

Topic	Clues	Author's Purpose
How to make a pinecone bird feeder	No entertaining words. No persuasive words. Details explaining how to make a pinecone bird feeder.	To explain how to make a pinecone bird feeder

Try This Strategy

Monitor and Clarify

When you **monitor and clarify,** you check your understanding of the main ideas and details in a passage.

- Pause after you read each paragraph. Make sure you understand the ideas in each paragraph.
- Clarify ideas in the text by restating them in your own words.
- Reread the text to clarify ideas you do not understand.

Read the passage. Use the Reading Guide for tips that can help you monitor and clarify and determine the author's purpose as you read.

Reading Guide

Read the title and first paragraph. What do you think the passage will be about?

What important ideas did you read about in the middle paragraphs? Restate these ideas in your own words.

What do you think the author's purpose was for writing this passage?

How to Make a Pinecone Bird Feeder

Bird feeders are a great way to give birds the extra food they need. You can make a bird feeder using a pinecone and a few other materials. Here is how to make your own pinecone bird feeder.

First go outside and find some large pinecones. Tie a string around the stem of each pinecone. You will use these strings to hang the bird feeders.

Now put the pinecones aside. Mix half a cup of vegetable oil and half a cup of dry oatmeal in a large bowl. Instead of oatmeal, you can also use peanut butter or other sticky foods. Stir the mixture well. This mixture will cover about three or four pinecones.

Spread the mixture over the pinecones using a butter knife. You can also use the back side of a spoon. Once the pinecones are coated, you are ready for the birdseed.

Pour birdseed into a pie tin or paper plate. You may wish to add bread crumbs or other foods in with the birdseed. Roll the pinecones around in the birdseed until they are covered. Now you have your very own bird feeders! Hang the bird feeders outside on nearby tree branches.

Now use what you learned to determine the author's purpose.

Answer the questions on the next page.

Practice the Skill 2

Practice determining the author's purpose by answering questions about the article you just read. Read each question. Circle the letter of the best answer.

1. What does the title suggest about the author's main purpose for writing?

    A   It suggests that the author will describe different bird feeders.

    B   It suggests that the author will persuade readers to build a bird feeder.

    C   It suggests that the author will explain how to make a bird feeder.

    D   It suggests that the author will entertain readers with a story about making bird feeders.

2. The third paragraph of this passage provides —

    A   facts about making a pinecone bird feeder

    B   fun stories about homemade bird feeders

    C   facts about birds

    D   the author's opinion on bird feeders

3. Which words best describe this passage?

    A   sad and gloomy

    B   fun and exciting

    C   angry and forceful

    D   factual and direct

4. This passage is best described as —

    A   an entertaining story

    B   a persuasive article

    C   a factual article

    D   a journal entry

5. The author's purpose is —

    A   to entertain you

    B   to explain how to do something

    C   to convince you of something

    D   to describe something

6. On a separate sheet of paper, explain the differences between a passage that informs and a passage that entertains.

STICK SHIP

Rob McDonald's ship is made of ice cream sticks.

AMSTERDAM, THE NETHERLANDS— Set sail for ice cream! "Captain Rob" McDonald has found a new use for ice cream sticks. The former Hollywood stuntman used 15 million wooden ice cream sticks to build a 50-foot-long model of a Viking ship. McDonald spent two years and used over two tons of glue putting together the 13-ton ship.

But McDonald is more than just a shipbuilder. He is also president of the Sea Heart Foundation, which creates **delightful** building projects for children in hospitals all over the world. "I have a dream to show children they can do anything," said McDonald before launching the ship for the first time in August 2005. "If they can dream it, they can do it."

As for his next dream, McDonald says he'd like to sail the ship across the Atlantic Ocean, just as the Vikings did 1,000 years ago. The ship is currently on display at an antique ship show near his home in Amsterdam, capital of the Netherlands.

Write About It

Reread the article carefully. Is the author's purpose to inform, persuade, or entertain? Use clues from the article to support your answer.

Read this passage about school sports teams. Then answer the questions on the next page.

Join a School Sports Team Today!

My school has many different sports teams. There's basketball, field hockey, soccer, and many others. Joining a school sports team is one of the best things you can do. I think everyone should join at least one sports team at school.

First of all, playing sports is a great way to get exercise. If I weren't playing sports, I would probably just be sitting around. It is much better to be active. I always feel better when I'm exercising. I'm sure everyone else feels the same way.

Joining a sports team is also a great way to make friends. Some of my best friends are on the soccer team I joined. My teammates and I go to my house to hang out after practice. We also go out to dinner together after each game. You will make so many great friends if you join a team.

Playing on a team has also taught me about leadership and teamwork. I'm always teaching my younger teammates about how to play the game. It is a lot of work, but it has taught me how to be a leader. My teammates and I have also learned how to work together. I believe that teamwork is very important. Joining a team is the best way to learn about both teamwork and leadership.

Playing on a sports team is also a lot of fun. Everyone loves playing games, and sports games are the best! You get to play with lots of other people, which makes it more fun. You also have other people watching you play and cheering you on. It is so much fun playing a game with a crowd cheering you on.

There are so many great sports teams you can join. I bet that everyone can find at least one that they like. So go ahead! Join a school sports team today!

Read each question. Circle the letter of the best answer.

1. What is the first paragraph mostly about?

    A which school sports team to join

    B how to join a school sports team

    C why joining a school sports team is great

    D why joining a school sports team is wrong

2. What are the middle paragraphs mostly about?

    A reasons why you should join a school sports team

    B facts about different school sports teams

    C a story about playing on a school sports team

    D how to play different school sports

3. In the first paragraph, the phrase *I think* shows that the author is telling —

    A a fact

    B an explanation

    C a story

    D an opinion

4. Which of the following sentences from the article does not state an opinion?

    A I think everyone should join at least one sports team at school.

    B Some of my best friends are on the soccer team I joined.

    C I believe that teamwork is very important.

    D I bet that everyone can find at least one that they like.

5. Which word from the article shows that the author might be giving an opinion?

    A joining

    B teamwork

    C believe

    D leadership

6. The author's opinion seems to be that —

    A school sports teams are terrific

    B school sports teams are boring

    C school sports teams are terrible

    D school sports teams are silly

7. What is the author's purpose in writing this article?

    A to give facts about school sports teams only

    B to entertain you with sports stories

    C to describe how to join a school sports team

    D to convince you to join a school sports team

8. Choose three sentences from the article that state opinions. On a separate sheet of paper, explain what words or clues helped you determine that the author stated an opinion.

Show What You Know

Before you begin this lesson, take this quiz to show what you know about problems and solutions. First, read this story about Maria. Then answer the questions that follow.

MARIA SAVES THE DAY

Maria sat in the back of the boat as her older brother Joe rowed toward the island. She was going to collect shells for a school project.

Once they were close to shore, Joe said, "Okay, Maria, hop out and start looking for shells. I'll tie the boat over by those trees."

Maria grabbed her pail and **waded** to shore.

Suddenly, Joe let out a yelp. "What's wrong?" Maria cried.

"My arm!" Joe groaned. "I've been stung! I was tying the boat to this stump, and a bee came out!"

"We have to go back home. You might need medicine," Maria said.

"But I can't row," Joe moaned, clutching his arm in pain.

"No problem. I'm not as big as you, but I can take us home."

Joe climbed into the boat. Then Maria jumped in and pushed off from shore.

The rowing was hard, but Maria kept going. Finally, they reached the dock. "Mom, we need help!" Maria shouted. "Joe was stung by a bee!"

Maria's mother ran toward them. Maria smiled to herself. She had done it! She had brought Joe to safety.

Circle the letter of the best answer.

1. What is the main problem Maria and Joe face in the story?

   A Maria needs shells for a project.

   B Maria and Joe row to an island.

   C Joe doesn't want to row the boat to shore.

   D Joe is stung by a bee.

2. Why doesn't Joe row the boat home?

   A He is tired.

   B His arm hurts too much.

   C The water is too choppy.

   D He says that it is Maria's turn to row.

3. How does Maria help Joe?

   A She uses first aid to treat his injury.

   B She collects shells for her project.

   C She shouts for her mother to help.

   D She rows the boat and takes them home.

4. Why does Maria smile to herself?

   A Her mother is glad to see them.

   B Her mother is a doctor.

   C She has saved the day.

   D She says something funny.

Guided Instruction 1

Introduction

Many articles and stories have **problems and solutions.** A **problem** is something that causes trouble. A **solution** is how the problem is solved.

To identify problems and solutions,

- Look for something that causes trouble for a person or character.
- Look for the steps taken to solve the problem.
- Decide what action or event makes the problem go away. This is the solution. Was the solution successful?

Here's How

Read these sentences. What is Jason's problem? How might it be solved?

When I got there, Jason looked miserable. I showed him the magic tricks I learned. He smiled a little but still didn't seem happy.

Think About It

1. Jason looked miserable. The problem is that he is not happy.

2. The narrator showed Jason some magic tricks to make him feel better.

3. Jason did not seem happy. The solution was not successful.

Use Prior Knowledge

When you **use prior knowledge,** you think about what you already know about a topic. You use this to help you understand what you read.

- Before reading, think about the topic. Ask yourself what you already know about this topic.
- As you read, think about what is happening. Think about situations in your own life that are like the problems in the story.
- Use your own knowledge and experiences to find the problem and solution in the passage you are reading.

Read the story. Use the Reading Guide for tips. The tips will help you use prior knowledge and identify problems and solutions as you read.

Reading Guide

Think about what you know about having chicken pox. Use what you know to understand why this is causing a problem.

Look for steps the narrator took to solve the problem.

Think about how Jason's mood changed from the beginning of the story to the end of the story.

A Sick Joke

Last week, my friend Jason caught the chicken pox. He had red spots everywhere. He had to stay inside because chicken pox is **contagious.** His mom didn't want him to make anyone else sick. Jason didn't like staying inside all day and was really bored.

I felt sorry for Jason. I wanted to cheer him up, so I headed over to his house.

When I got there, Jason looked miserable. I showed him the magic tricks I learned. He smiled a little but still didn't seem happy. Then, I took out my baseball cards and asked him to make some trades. Usually he loves to do that but not this time. Finally, I thought of something that was sure to distract him. He loves practical jokes.

I went into the other room with my markers. Then I colored my face and arms with little red dots. I marched back in and said, "Now we can have the chicken pox together." Jason laughed, and we enjoyed ourselves for the rest of the afternoon.

Now use what you learned to identify problems and solutions.

Answer the questions on the next page.

Practice identifying problems and solutions in the story you just read.

EXAMPLE

What is one thing the narrator does to try to solve Jason's problem?

A He loans Jason his bicycle.

B He reads a story to Jason.

C He shows Jason a magic trick.

D He catches the chicken pox.

Look for something that's causing trouble for the characters.

Jason is sick.

Think about what the narrator does to try to solve the problem.

He does magic tricks, trades baseball cards, and plays a joke on Jason.

Think about whether the solution was successful.

Although the narrator tries to cheer up Jason with a magic trick, this solution is not successful.

Now read each question. Circle the letter of the best answer.

1. To Jason, what is the worst problem caused by being sick?

   A He has to miss school.

   B He can't ride his bicycle.

   C He can't go outside.

   D He has red spots.

2. What trouble has this problem caused?

   A Jason feels tired.

   B Jason feels bored.

   C Jason feels ugly.

   D Jason feels angry.

3. What action solves the problem?

   A The narrator performs a magic trick.

   B The narrator trades baseball cards with Jason.

   C The narrator tells Jason a story.

   D The narrator plays a joke on Jason.

4. Why does the narrator trade baseball cards with Jason?

   A Jason has a baseball card he wants.

   B The narrator wants to cheer Jason up.

   C Jason has been asking him to trade baseball cards.

   D The narrator does not have many baseball cards.

BRIDGE FOR SALE FOR $1

Get out your wallets! New York's Willis Avenue Bridge is for sale for $1.

NEW YORK, NY—One of New York's oldest bridges is also its cheapest. The 105-year-old Willis Avenue Bridge in New York City went on sale recently for just $1. The bridge crosses the Harlem River and carries up to 75,000 cars a day from Manhattan to the Bronx. It was originally built for $2,500,000.

City officials are replacing the bridge with a new one. They were planning to simply tear down the Willis Avenue Bridge, but they could not because it is considered a **landmark.** To get around this problem, the bridge is being sold for just $1.

As part of the deal, officials will deliver the 3,000-foot bridge by boat 15 miles in either direction. Since the bridge is so large, it will be delivered piece by piece. So far, the city has not received any offers, but they still have plenty of time. The Willis Avenue Bridge will stay open until a new bridge takes its place in 2012.

Write About It

Now you will practice the skill using a real news story. Complete this graphic organizer by filling in the box that leads to this solution.

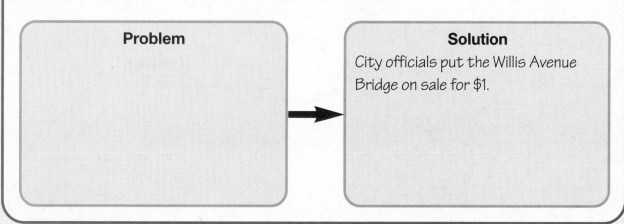

Problem		Solution
	→	City officials put the Willis Avenue Bridge on sale for $1.

Ladder to Success

Review

You have learned that a **problem** is something that causes trouble. The **solution** is an action that solves the problem.

Review the steps that help identify problems and solutions.

- As you read, look for the things that cause trouble in the story or article.
- Think about what is done to try to solve the problem. Think about how these actions might help solve the problem.
- Find the event, step, or idea that solves the problem. Think about whether the solution was successful or not.

Practice 1

Read the following passage. As you read, find the problem that scientists face. How do they hope to solve that problem?

> For a long time, people have searched for signs of life in space. Are there living things on other planets? Scientists have scanned for radio signals. They thought that was the best way to detect aliens. However, they have found no signs of life.
>
> Now scientists have a new idea. They think that aliens may use laser beams. Through these flashes of light, aliens might send messages. Scientists made a machine that can detect lasers in space. Perhaps an alien will send us a flash or two!

List the problem that scientists are trying to solve in the first box. Write how they are trying to solve the problem in the second box.

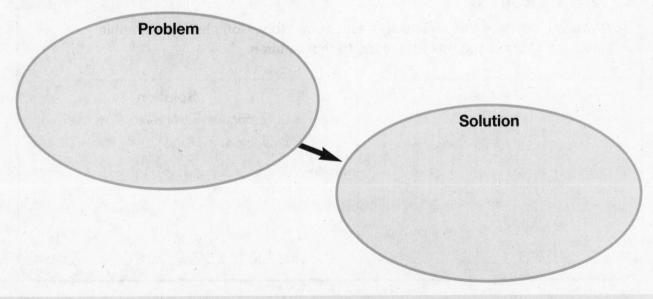

Duplicating any part of this book is prohibited by law.

Practice 2

Read the passage. Look for problems and solutions.

A man took a large sum of money out of his bank account. He brought it home but was nervous. He had to find a safe place for it. He searched around the house. Finally, he had a great solution. He hid the money in a trashcan.

Then, something **unexpected** happened. The man forgot to tell his wife about the money. She put the trashcan on the curb. Workers took the trash, and the money, to the dump.

The man called the police. He told them how much money it was. He described the bag. He told them the name of his bank. The police searched until they found it. It was a lucky day for that man!

Complete the graphic organizer below to show the problems and solutions. In the boxes on the left, write how the man solved the problem of where to hide the money. In the boxes on the right, write how he solved the problem of finding the money.

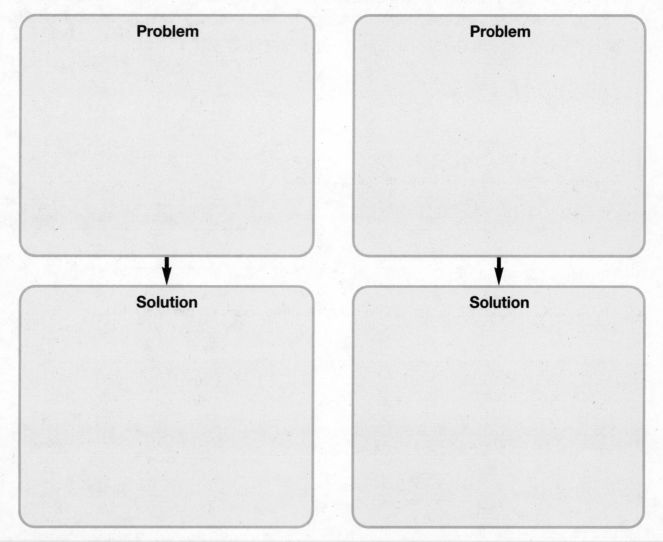

Practice 3

Read the passage. Then identify the problems and solutions to answer the questions. Make a graphic organizer on a separate sheet of paper to organize your thoughts.

Kate and her mom had moved into a new apartment. They were really excited but knew they had plenty of work to do to make it feel like home.

"Your bedroom needs the most work," Mom said. "It's dusty and dull. Let's start there." First, they scrubbed the walls and floor. Then they went to the wallpaper store. Kate picked out yellow wallpaper with a lively design. It was just the thing to brighten the walls of her room.

They worked together, measuring and cutting the paper. They started pasting along the edge of each wall and worked toward the middle. When they were almost finished, Kate realized they'd made a mistake. They didn't have enough paper to finish the job. Now there was a square of white in the center of one wall.

Kate thought for a few minutes. Then she unpacked one of her boxes. She pulled out her favorite picture, a large framed photo taken on her vacation with her dad. She hung it over the white space on the wall. It looked perfect!

1. What problem do Kate and her mom have with Kate's bedroom?

2. What problem occurs while they are wallpapering?

3. Why does Kate hang the framed photo over the white space on the wall?

Duplicating any part of this book is prohibited by law.

Guided Instruction 2

Introduction

The main events of a story, and the main ideas in an article, often present **problems and solutions.** A **problem** is something that causes trouble. The **solution** is what makes the trouble go away.

As you saw on pages 139–141, graphic organizers can help you identify each problem and solution that occurs in a story or article.

- In the first box, describe the problem.
- In the second box, write the action or event that solves the problem.

Here's How

Read these sentences. What problem did the people face? How did they solve it?

In Pakistan, scientists have found the remains of a town that is more than 9,000 years old. When they studied the peoples' bones, they found something surprising. Some of the people had problems with their teeth. It looked as if the people had been to the dentist to fix them!

Think About It

Problem	Solution
The people had a problems with their teeth.	They went to the dentist to fix them.

Try This Strategy

Scan and Skim

When you **scan and skim,** you look over a passage before you read it. This gives you a sense of what it is about. Key words may give hints about the problem and solution.

- Before reading, look at the title and any pictures. Is this fiction or nonfiction? What is the topic?
- Skim over the passage quickly, looking for key words. What is the problem? What solutions might make that problem go away?
- Keep the answers to the questions in mind as you read the passage carefully.

Read the article. Use the Reading Guide for tips that can help you scan and skim and identify problems and solutions.

Reading Guide

Look over the passage for key words. What do the words suggest about the topic of the article?

What might have caused trouble for the ancient people?

Think about what the people used the drill for. What different problems did the drill solve?

Can you find what caused the problems the people faced?

Ancient Trips to the Dentist

In Pakistan, scientists have found the remains of a town that is more than 9,000 years old. When they studied the peoples' bones, they found something surprising. Some of the people had problems with their teeth. It looked as if the people had been to the dentist to fix them!

Holes had been drilled into many people's teeth. Inside the holes, scientists found ridges. The ridges were cut with a drill. At a nearby site, scientists found tiny drill heads made of flint. They also found stone beads. The beads had holes in them that made it possible to string them together. The people probably used the same drills to make holes in beads as in their teeth!

The scientists think the people saw the dentist for tooth decay, as we do today. They found remains of decay in some teeth. They also found signs of harsh wear and tear. The people at that site grew wheat. They ground it into flour with sharp stones. Slivers of stone fell into the flour. Then the people baked bread. When they ate it, stone slivers wore down their teeth.

This discovery really surprised the scientists. They never imagined that 9,000 years ago, people understood how to care for teeth.

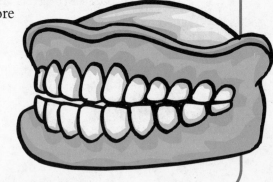

Now use what you learned to identify problems and solutions.

Answer the questions on the next page.

Practice the Skill 2

Practice identifying problems and solutions by answering questions about the article you just read. Read each question. Circle the letter of the best answer.

1. What problem did these ancient people have?

   A bad teeth

   B painful wounds

   C lack of food

   D lack of tools

2. How did they attempt to solve the problem?

   A They planted wheat.

   B They traded beads.

   C They ground wheat with sharp stones.

   D They went to a dentist.

3. What process was used to solve the problem?

   A pulling the teeth

   B drilling the teeth

   C grinding the wheat

   D making beads to trade and sell

4. What caused the people's teeth to decay more quickly?

   A They had slivers of stone in their food.

   B They ate wheat.

   C They ate lots of sweets.

   D They ground wheat with their teeth.

5. What is another way the drills may have solved a problem for the people?

   A They made it possible to string beads together.

   B They made it possible to create beads.

   C They made it possible to grind wheat.

   D They made it possible to bake bread.

6. Today, dentists are much more successful at solving problems with painful teeth. On a separate sheet of paper, write why today's dentists are better at solving these problems.

WHALE LOST
on Delaware River

A beluga whale got lost on the Delaware River.

TRENTON, NJ—Even whales can take a wrong turn. A beluga whale named Helis got lost in the Delaware River near Trenton, New Jersey. The 10- to 12-foot whale swam over 80 miles away from his home in the Atlantic Ocean.

Experts are unsure how Helis got so far off course. Their biggest concern was for the young whale's health. Whales are better suited to salt water. They worried that Helis would struggle in the fresh water of the Delaware River.

Experts hoped the white whale would return to the ocean by himself. "His best chances lie with letting nature take its course," said Dr. Janet Whaley, a marine veterinarian. "We've ruled out a live capture for now."

Helis is not the first whale to get lost on the Delaware River. Waldo the Wrong-Way Whale, as he was called by Philadelphia residents, swam in the river in 1995. He eventually made it back to the ocean.

Write About It

On a separate sheet of paper, write a brief paragraph. First, explain Helis's problem. Then, explain the solution that experts have come up with so far.

Read this passage about a clever man. Then answer the questions on the next page.

Rube Goldberg

Rube Goldberg was a unique artist. He drew cartoons that showed the trouble with silly and difficult ways of doing simple tasks. He had an enjoyable career. He got to use his drawing skills to make people laugh and think.

When Rube was four years old, he knew very little about drawing. As a result, he traced pictures in books and magazines. Soon, his drawings got better. The only trouble was that he couldn't buy all the magazines he wanted to trace. At eight, he helped a friend deliver magazines. His friend paid him with free magazines. Then Rube ran home and traced the pictures.

Rube's father sent him to college for **engineering.** After college, Rube needed money to pay his bills. He found a job where he could make a lot of money working as an engineer. The money was good, but Rube was unhappy. His talent was for drawing, and he wanted to use that talent. So he quit the engineering job and went to work for a newspaper. He loved it. They paid him to draw cartoons!

As a cartoonist, Rube needed lots of new ideas about what to draw. So he drew about what he knew. He had worked as an engineer, and he used that. His best cartoon character was an engineer. The character invented machines. Did the machines do useful things? No! They did easy things in very complicated ways.

One machine licked stamps. First, a robot put a sheet of stamps on a table. The gum side was up. Then the robot dropped a can of ants onto the stamps. An anteater stuck out its long tongue and licked up the ants. In the process, he also licked the stamps!

Another machine sharpened pencils. A woodpecker would do the job, but not until after several other things happened. In part, the smoke from an iron burning pants drives an opposum from its hole. Its fall into a basket pulls a string, lifting a cage to free a woodpecker to peck a pencil.

He loved to make fun of people who did simple things in complicated ways. Today, Rube's name is in the dictionary. A *Rube Goldberg* is a silly, complicated way to do a simple task.

Read each question. Circle the letter of the best answer.

1. What problem did Rube have with magazines?

   A He was forced to deliver magazines.

   B He didn't like magazines.

   C He couldn't buy enough magazines to trace.

   D He spent all his money on magazines.

2. What did Rube do to solve his problem with magazines?

   A He ran away from home.

   B He agreed and did what he was told.

   C He stopped tracing from magazines.

   D He delivered magazines for his friend.

3. Why did Rube get a job as an engineer?

   A He needed money to pay his bills.

   B He loved engineering.

   C It was a perfect chance for him to draw.

   D He wanted to design airplanes.

4. What problem did Rube have with his job as an engineer?

   A The job didn't pay well.

   B The job was too far away.

   C The job was boring.

   D The job was too difficult.

5. What did he do to solve his problem with his job as an engineer?

   A He quit and went to work as a cartoonist.

   B He asked for a raise.

   C He began drawing in his spare time.

   D He quit and got a job selling magazines.

6. The article describes a complicated machine that uses a robot. What simple problem did it solve?

   A It fed hungry ants.

   B It put another robot to work.

   C It handled postage stamps.

   D It captured a runaway anteater.

7. The article describes a complicated machine that uses a woodpecker. What simple problem did it solve?

   A It watered the lawn.

   B It made pencils.

   C It sharpened pencils.

   D It opened a door.

8. Rube Goldberg created his drawings because he saw a problem with the way some people do things. On a separate sheet of paper, tell what this problem was.

Glossary

author's purpose the reason that an author writes a story (Lesson 9)

ban to stop people from doing something (Lesson 3)

biscuit a small piece of bread (Lesson 2)

booty things that are stolen (Lesson 3)

cause and effect a cause is an event that makes something happen; the effect is what happens (Lesson 3)

challenging difficult (Lesson 9)

chisel a sharp metal tool used to cut and shape stone (Lesson 2)

climate the weather that a place usually has (Lesson 3)

collide to crash into something (Lesson 1)

compare and contrast to find ways things are alike and different (Lesson 1)

conclusion an idea you figure out from details you read (Lesson 6)

condition the way something is (Lesson 5)

contagious ability of a disease to be passed from one person to another through touching or other contact (Lesson 10)

container ship a boat that carries boxes of things that will later be sold (Lesson 2)

context clues words that help you figure out the meaning of words that you don't know (Lesson 4)

contribute to give money or time to a person or group (Lesson 7)

delightful causing enjoyment (Lesson 9)

director a person who manages the making of a movie (Lesson 1)

draw conclusions to figure out what the author wants you to understand from details

you read in a passage and what you already know about the subject (Lesson 6)

encounter an unexpected meeting (Lesson 6)

engineering jobs that use science and math to build things, such as bridges and roads (Lesson 10)

ensure to make sure that something will happen (Lesson 2)

facial a series of things done to the face to make it more beautiful, usually including cleansing and massage (Lesson 2)

figurative language words that create an image in a reader's mind (Lesson 7)

footpath a trail that people use to walk from one place to another (Lesson 1)

identify to see something and say what it is (Lesson 5)

impress to cause someone to feel admiration and respect (Lesson 8)

ingredient something that is part of a mixture (Lesson 2)

inseparable always together and difficult to get apart (Lesson 1)

landmark a place that is famous for its history (Lesson 10)

main idea and details the most important idea or event of a passage or paragraph and the facts or events that support it (Lesson 5)

make-believe people, places, things, and events that could not exist in real life (Lesson 8)

marine having to do with the sea (Lesson 3)

moisten to make wet (Lesson 2)

monitor and clarify to make sure that you understand what you are reading (Lesson 1, Lesson 4, Lesson 9)

mutiny an act of taking control from leaders, usually through violence (Lesson 3)

nutrition the study of food and how it affects people's health (Lesson 3)

orphan to have one's parents taken away (Lesson 1)

outlandish noticeably strange (Lesson 9)

patent permission given by the government to be the only one to make money from an invention (Lesson 2)

plunder to steal from a place using violence (Lesson 3)

precious valuable and rare (Lesson 3)

predict to think about what you have read and what might happen next (Lesson 3, Lesson 6, Lesson 9)

problems and solutions a problem is something that causes trouble; a solution is how the problem is solved (Lesson 10)

real people, places, and things that exist or could exist in real life (Lesson 8)

recognize to look at someone and know who they are (Lesson 3)

recruit to get people to join a group (Lesson 3)

retirement the time in a person's life after they have stopped working at a job (Lesson 5)

sanctuary a place where animals are protected from hunters and other animals (Lesson 1)

satellite a machine put into space that moves in circles around the Earth (Lesson 5)

scan and skim to look through a passage quickly to get an idea of what it is about or to find a particular part (Lesson 2, Lesson 5, Lesson 10)

sensor a part of a machine that responds to things around it (Lesson 5)

sequence the order in which things happen (Lesson 2)

shortening fat that is used in baking (Lesson 2)

species a type or class of animal (Lesson 6)

splotch an oddly-shaped spot (Lesson 7)

summarize to retell the most important parts of a story or passage in your own words (Lesson 2, Lesson 5, Lesson 6)

swine a pig (Lesson 8)

trend something that is popular at a given time (Lesson 6)

unexpected not expected; surprising (Lesson 10)

use prior knowledge to use what you know to understand what you read (Lesson 1, Lesson 7, Lesson 8, Lesson 10)

visualize to picture in your mind what you are reading (Lesson 3, Lesson 4, Lesson 7, Lesson 8)

wade to walk through water (Lesson 10)

wisecrack something that is said for the purpose of being funny or clever (Lesson 7)

Notes

Graphic Organizers

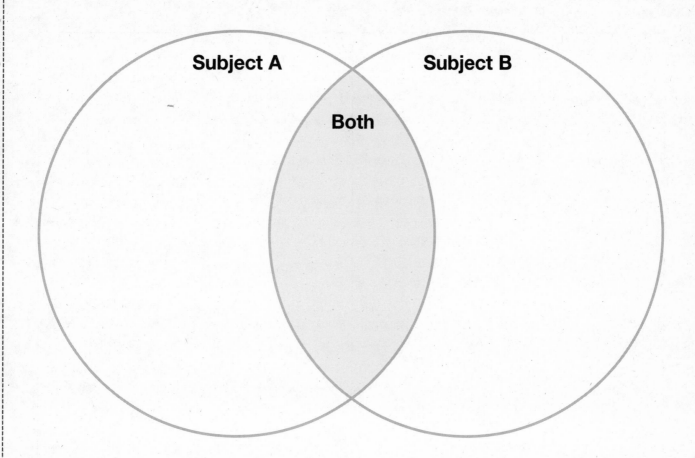

Remove Graphic Organizers Here ◄

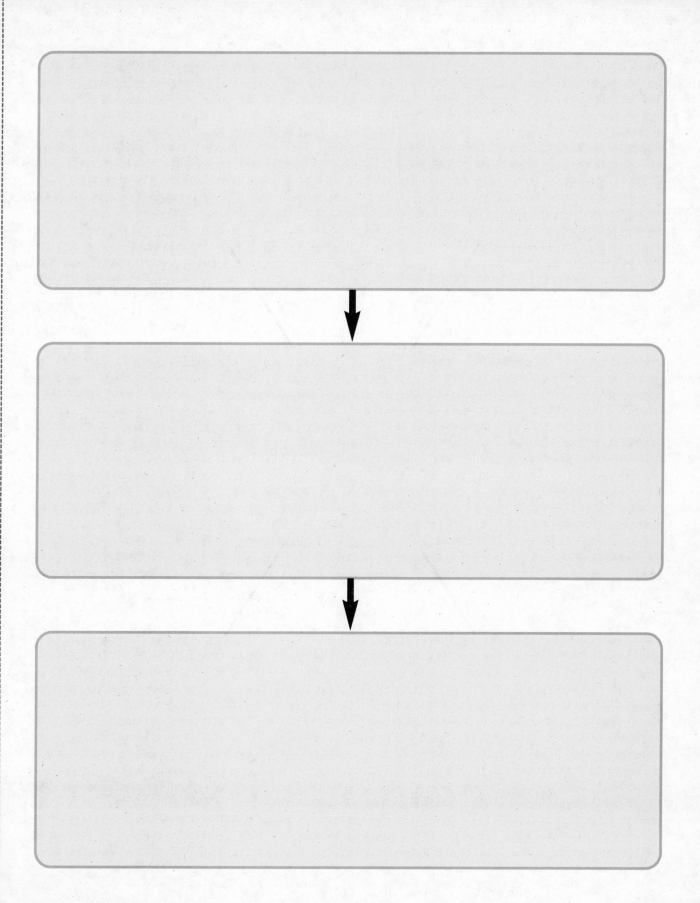

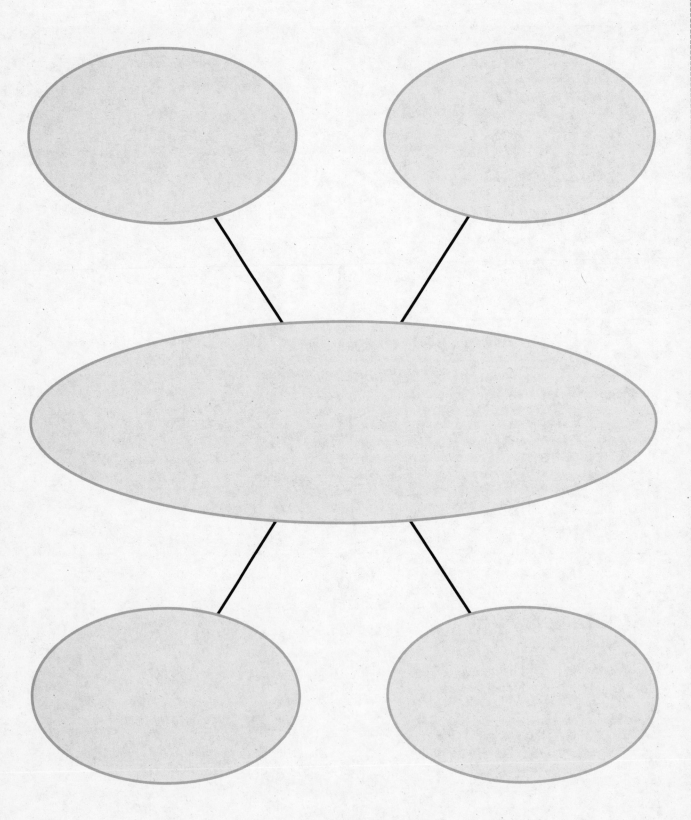

1.

2.

3.

4.

5.

6.

7.

8.

9.

10.

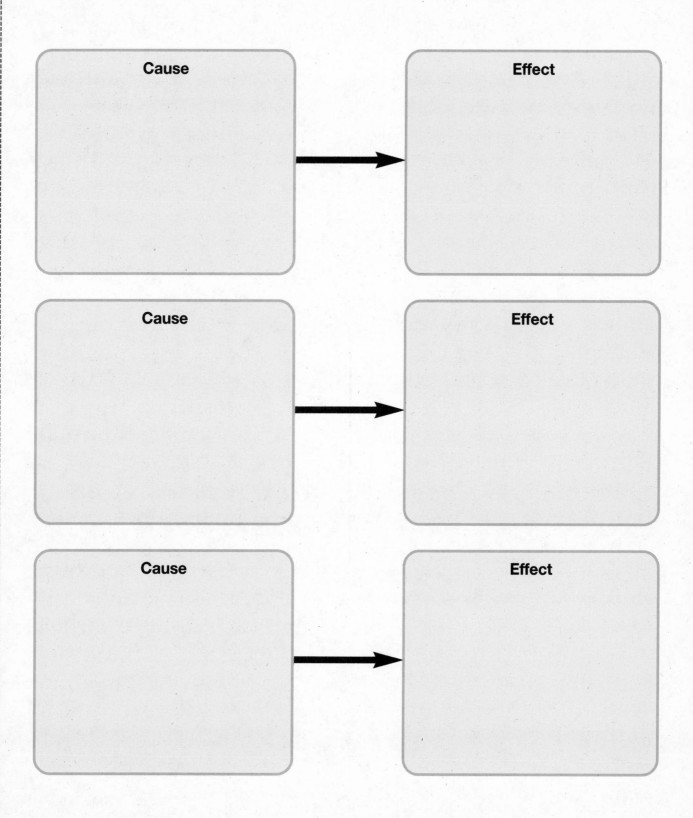

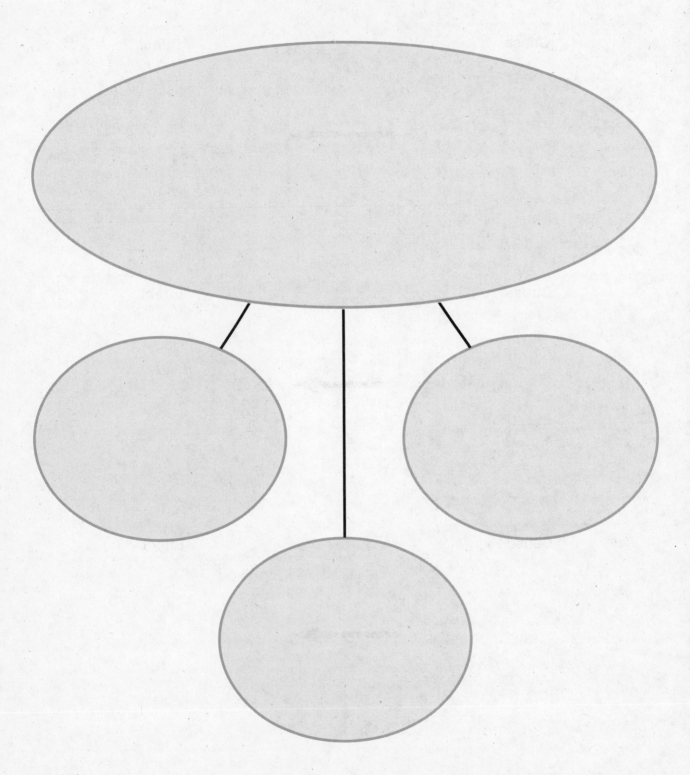